MARRIED LOVE

Marie Stopes was born in 1880 and educated in Edinburgh and London. In 1921 she founded the world's first birth-control clinic, in London.

Her writings included plays, poetry and scientific works on palaeobotany. Her most famous books are *Married Love, Wise Parenthood* and *Radiant Motherhood*.

She died in 1958.

Marie Carmichael Stopes

MARRIED LOVE

A NEW CONTRIBUTION TO THE
SOLUTION OF SEX DIFFICULTIES

With an Introduction by Dr John Peel

VICTOR GOLLANCZ

LONDON

First published in Great Britain 1918
by A. C. Fifield
13 Clifford's Inn, London EC4

This Gollancz Paperbacks edition first published 1995
by Victor Gollancz
An imprint of the Cassell Group
Wellington House, 125 Strand, London WC2R 0BB

Twenty-ninth edition

© the Galton Institute

A catalogue record for this book is
available from the British Library.

ISBN 0 575 06273 8

Photoset in Great Britain by
Rowland Phototypesetting Ltd, Bury St Edmunds, Suffolk
Printed in Great Britain by
Guernsey Press Co. Ltd, Guernsey, Channel Isles

Dedicated to young husbands and all those who are
betrothed in love

Contents

Introduction

BY JOHN PEEL

In 1935 a panel of distinguished American academics was asked to list the twenty-five most influential books published in the previous fifty years. *Married Love* was placed sixteenth of the twenty-five, just behind Frazer's *The Golden Bough* and Marx's *Das Kapital*, but ahead of Einstein's *Relativity*, Freud's *Interpretation of Dreams*, Hitler's *Mein Kampf* and Keynes' *Economic Consequences of the Peace*. *Married Love*, however, differed from all the other works chosen in that it sought directly to influence individual behaviour as well as to inform general thinking. It is a remarkable book written by an even more remarkable woman. The book is a classic of modern literature; its author was the founding genius of the English birth-control movement. Both book and author have a significant place in twentieth-century social history.

Published on 27 March 1918, *Married Love* sold two thousand copies within a fortnight of publication and, despite an acute wartime paper shortage, went through seven editions in its first year. During the next two decades more than a million copies were sold and the book was translated into fourteen languages and into Braille, bringing considerable wealth to its publishers. Yet before its acceptance by A. C. Fifield it had been rejected by at least two other publishers and Fifield had demanded, and received, from Marie Stopes a subsidy before publication of £200 (£4,800 in 1995).

The instant success of *Married Love* was unrelated to the

public notoriety which its author was subsequently to achieve, though that notoriety doubtless helped to sustain the book through its many editions. But in 1918 Marie Stopes was little known outside her own professional scientific discipline. She was thirty-seven years old, the survivor of a broken marriage – and a virgin. In 1911 she had married an academic colleague, Reginald Ruggles Gates, but the marriage had proved sexually unfulfilling and five years later she had successfully sued, as *virgo intacta*, to have it annulled. In the attempt, initially to save her marriage and subsequently to assemble the necessary evidence for her annulment proceedings, she had begun to explore the existing literature on the physiological, psychological and cultural aspects of sexual relationships. Over a period of at least two years, spent almost entirely in the Reading Room of the British Museum, she studied everything then published in English, French and German; she may, according to Dr C. P. Blacker, have been the only person ever to have read all seven volumes of Havelock Ellis's *Studies in the Psychology of Sex*.

By 1914 she had resolved to publish the results of her research as a book, in order to save others from 'the misery, humiliation and frustration' which she had endured. 'It would be a book on marriage and sex and it would teach a man and a woman how to understand each other's sexual problems. It would not be presented as a scientific textbook or it would defeat its purpose to help ordinary people who required a book simply, even emotionally, written, but it must be scientifically based on the truths of sex.' The terms of such a prospectus explain both the historical originality and the uneven literary style of *Married Love*. Its promise was the liberating sublimity of mutually orgasmic marital coitus; the means to its achievement a sophisticated knowledge of sexual physiology. Neither had an established literature or, therefore, an accepted vocabulary. The vernacular of phallocentric pornography and the euphemistic prose of the romantic novel were alike inadequate to any serious discussion of coital orgasm (which in any case only *French* novels permitted to women). An even greater problem lay in the discussion of those bodily processes and events where myth and taboo, as well as the threat of the Obscene Publications Act, had long been a deterrent to serious scholarship. Ellis's books had to be published abroad; and the editors of the sixth edition (1915) of T. H. Huxley's *Elementary Physiology* still thought it wise to omit any mention of the reproductive system. That, despite this dual handicap, Marie Stopes was able to fulfil her ambition – to produce a book which, she predicted, would 'electrify England' – and to write a text which, through twenty-eight editions in thirty-seven years, survived virtually unamended, qualifies *Married Love* as a literary landmark.

The reason why *Married Love* found such a vast, immediate and receptive readership was correctly stated by its author, writing some years later: 'It crashed into English society like a bombshell,' she recalled, 'its explosively contagious main theme – that woman like man has the same physiological reaction, a reciprocal need for enjoyment and benefit from union in marriage distinct from the exercise of maternal functions – made Victorian husbands gasp.' English society in 1918 was of course still dominated by Victorian prejudices, especially those relating to sex. The double standard which condoned, in men, an acknowledged licentiousness underlying the outward veneer of respectability had the effect of dividing women into two distinct species: the sexually anaesthetised wife and the loose woman. This double standard was socially enshrined in attitudes to education, employment and health; it was also reflected in property and divorce legislation. The 1857 Matrimonial Causes Act, for example, permitted divorce on the petition of the husband on the grounds of a single act of adultery on the part of his wife; a wife, however, in order to divorce her husband had to prove that his adultery was accompanied by some aggravating offence – cruelty, desertion, venereal disease or sodomy. Between 1858 and 1900 an annual average of five hundred divorces were granted in England and Wales; only a small proportion of these were granted on the petition of the wife.

Marie Stopes was a product of Victorian society who had successfully overcome many of the obstacles which limited the ambitions of women. Born in 1880 to professional, though enlightened, parents, she attended schools in Edinburgh and London before entering University College where she completed the normal three-year degree course in two years, gaining a gold medal in her first year and graduating at the head of her (otherwise all-male) year in 1902 with first-class honours in Botany. In 1903 she undertook post-graduate work at the University of Munich, gaining her Doctor of Philosophy degree in 1904 on the basis of a thesis written in German. The following year she became the first woman to be appointed to the lecturing staff in the science faculty at the University of Manchester and, gaining her D.Sc. in that year, she was the youngest doctor of science in Britain. She was subsequently awarded a Royal Society grant to carry out research in Japan and by 1918 had published a number of definitive monographs in palaeobotany. She had also, as we have seen, managed to circumvent, to her own advantage, the restraints of the divorce laws, and by the time *Married Love* was published she was remarried to a husband, the aeronautical pioneer H. V. Roe, whose wealth would enable her to devote the rest of her life to writing and public service.

Thus equipped by personal experience to understand the cultural obstacles preventing women from achieving either social or marital equality, Marie Stopes understood, too, that the First World War had created the possibility of a transition to a culture based on very different values. The war had, to some extent, mitigated the iniquities of Victorian England. The notorious Contagious Diseases Act was already repealed; the Sex Disqualification Removal Act abolished a number of barriers to education and employment; and in 1918 women over thirty were given the vote. Moreover, the war brought about changes in the occupational structure that were to have a lasting effect on attitudes. A million women were recruited for work in the factories or on the land; a further hundred thousand joined the auxiliary services of the armed forces; whilst the number of women in domestic service declined by four hundred thousand. Sexual questions were, for the first time, forced into public discussion when it was reported that one in five of those in the armed forces suffered from venereal disease, and in 1917 condoms were issued to the army without a murmur of opposition. Nevertheless, as A. J. P. Taylor points out, 'Women got little joy from their marital relations and complained to the health workers that their husbands "used" them so many times a week ... wives were lucky to be given a housekeeping allowance ... in almost every occupation women were paid less than men ... it was hard for a woman to rise to the top.' Equality of the sexes in access to divorce was not to be enacted until 1923.

Once published, such criticisms as the book attracted were almost solely concerned with the infelicities which inevitably remained. Thus, Professor R. V. Wheeler thought that 'what must live as among the finest writing in the English language' was marred by 'a grisly word or a brutish sentence', whilst Naomi Mitchison referred to the book as 'a light in great darkness to many of us, though a light shining through a lantern which was possibly not in the best taste'. Bertrand and Dora Russell, whilst wholly approving of the book, nevertheless 'laughed aloud' over the idea that a man should be encouraged to view his wife 'in the clear water of her bath'. Marie Stopes accepted such criticism as a price worth paying for the book's success. She reported the story of a well-known London men's club where demand for the book was so great that members were restricted to one hour's reading at a time; 'though they often started out giggling,' she wrote, 'they quickly became serious'.

Uniquely, we possess the surviving written testimony of a large proportion of the early purchasers of *Married Love* who, having found its contents relevant to their lives, felt impelled to write to its author and say so or to seek her further advice. Tens of thousands of these letters have been preserved, in the form of sixty archive boxes containing three hundred files, and are available for study; also preserved is a letter from her publishers, enclosing 1,400 of such letters received in a period of three days, and complaining that he had to employ two additional clerks to deal with this 'never-ending and unprofitable' correspondence. Those who have studied this archive, which also contains copies of Marie Stopes' replies, have revealed that about forty per cent of the writers were men, that they represented 'an enormous diversity of class, occupation and locality' and that the overwhelming majority of those seeking advice asked for further information about birth control.

This is unsurprising. Birth control, though it receives only passing mention in *Married Love*, was nevertheless of central importance to its message and of fundamental concern to its author. This concern extended beyond the mere commonplace recognition that fear of pregnancy inhibited frequency, spontaneity and enjoyment of sexual intercourse. Birth control itself, Marie Stopes realised, was an impediment to the transformation of the sex act into a spiritually elevating, life-enhancing experience which, according to *Married Love*, would create a more perfect marriage, more perfect individuals and a more perfect society.

In a period when only forty per cent of all married couples used any form of contraception at all and when, amongst those who did, more than eighty per cent relied on coitus interruptus or the condom, the case for such an innovation had to be carefully promoted. This was the purpose of *Wise Parenthood*, the successor to *Married Love* – the technical supplement to that earlier sociological work. The typescript of *Wise Parenthood* was already completed when *Married Love* was published in March

1918. The first edition appeared in November 1918 and its sub-sequent publishing history falls only slightly short of the success of the earlier work, with total sales of three-quarters of a million copies and the usual foreign translations during its thirty years in print. Its early appearance following on the success of *Married Love* enabled its author to respond constructively to her thousands of enquirers for birth-control advice; she referred them to her new book.

In the early 1920s Marie Stopes was amongst the most successful authors of non-fiction or fiction in England. The overworked phrase 'household name' today means very little; Marie Stopes, by some strange uncommunicated agreement, had a recognized and ubiquitous household location: the wardrobe shelf. By the mid-1920s she was already memorialised in the children's playground ditty:

> Jeanie, Jeanie full of hopes
> Read a book by Marie Stopes
> But to judge from her condition
> She must have read the wrong edition.

On 18 April 1931 the *Week-end Review* published the results of a literary competition which had asked for the best imaginary deathbed saying appropriate to any well-known person dead or living. The first prize was awarded to the entry attributing to Dr Marie Stopes the epitaph: LET JOY BE UNCONFINED. It was a brilliant encapsulation of the message of *Married Love*.

Its author had, by then, become the dominant figure in the English birth-control movement. In 1921 she had founded the first birth-control clinic in the world, which served as a base for her many battles with the law, the medical profession, rival birth-control organisations and the Roman Catholic Church. On most of the issues in which she became embroiled she was vindicated; her opponents, unable to meet her arguments with fact or logic, resorted to personal malice. The sometime head of the rival Family Planning Association, Mrs Margaret Pyke, commented patronisingly: 'In a final estimate, Marie Stopes may well prove to have been one of the most outstanding influences of the twentieth century – a judgement with which, one feels sure, she would have been in complete agreement.' Beatrice Webb, with characteristic waspishness, referred to her as the '*virago intacta*'. By the beginning of the Second World War she had begun a gradual withdrawal from her clinic activities and a return to literature and poetry. She died in 1958.

Marie Stopes had, as we have seen, regarded birth control as the means to more significant ends; her final years were made unhappy by the realisation that she would be remembered solely as a birth-control pioneer. In an obituary published in the *New Statesman* on 31 January 1959 Ronald Blythe recalled that she had, some years before, expressed her bitterness at this prospect at a meeting of the Literary Society: 'She saw the world divided up between midgets and giants – and there were few giants these days. It was pure emotion which made the giants, the throbbing, rapturous chosen ones, and fear of emotion which ordained the midgets. She was sick to death of us all. She had taught the man in the street to heave overboard the prurience and taboos of centuries so that he could soar up into the ultimate fulfilment of bliss – and what had he done? The oaf had used her gift like an extra gadget in the lavatory.'

Dr John Peel has written extensively on birth control and its history and is a former Chairman of the Marie Stopes Memorial Foundation. He has taught in the Universities of Sheffield, Hull and York and is a Fellow of the Galton Institute.

REFERENCES

Box, Muriel, *The Trial of Marie Stopes*, London: Femina Books, 1967
Briant, Keith, *Marie Stopes: A Biography*, London: Hogarth Press, 1962
Fryer, Peter, *The Birth Controllers*, London: Secker & Warburg, 1965
Hall, Lesley A., *Hidden Anxieties: Male Sexuality, 1900–1950*, London: Polity
    Press, 1991

Hall, Ruth, *Dear Dr Stopes: Letters to Marie Stopes*, London: André Deutsch, 1967

Marie Stopes: A Biography, London: André Deutsch, 1977

Maude, Aylmer, *The Authorised Life of Marie C. Stopes*, London: Williams & Norgate, 1924

Marie Stopes, Her Work and Play, London: Putnam, 1933

Peel, John, and Malcolm Potts, *Textbook of Contraceptive Practice*, Cambridge: Cambridge University Press, 1969

Rose, June, *Marie Stopes and the Sexual Revolution*, London: Faber & Faber, 1992

Soloway, Richard A., *Birth Control and the Population Question in England 1877–1930*, University of North Carolina Press, 1982

Taylor, A. J. P., *English History 1914–1945*, Oxford: Oxford University Press, 1965

Taylor, Laurie, 'The Unfinished Sexual Revolution', *Journal of Biosocial Science* (1971), vol. 3, 473–492

A Note on the Text

The text of this volume is that of the now rare first printing of the first edition, published by A. C. Fifield on 27 March 1918. It remained unaltered, apart from the correction of typographical and other minor errors, through the six editions produced by the original publisher. The seventh edition was published by G. P. Putnam's Sons Ltd in May 1919 and was revised. The letter from Father Stanislaus St John SJ, which had been included in a futile attempt to deflect the opposition of the Catholic Church, was now deleted, together with Marie Stopes' reply. This was the format which, with only minor subsequent revisions, was to continue until its final (twenty-eighth) edition in 1955, since when it has been out of print. Hogarth Press replaced Putnam as publisher in 1952.

The first edition was printed by A. C. Fifield's American associates in 1918, with alterations which Marie Stopes had not approved; it was nevertheless banned under the notorious Comstock laws and did not appear in the United States until 1923. Other overseas printings in English were undertaken in Australia, Canada and India. Translations were produced in Afrikaans, Arabic, Chinese, Czech, Danish, Norwegian, Dutch, German, Hungarian, Hindi, Italian, Romanian, Spanish and Swedish. The definitive bibliography of all of Marie Stopes' published works is *Marie Stopes: A Checklist of her Writings* by Peter Eaton and Marilyn Warnick (Croom Helm, London, 1977).

MARRIED LOVE

Preface

BY MISS JESSIE MURRAY, MB, BS

In this little book Dr Marie Stopes deals with subjects which are generally regarded as too sacred for an entirely frank treatment. Some earnest and delicate minds may feel apprehensive that such frankness in details is 'dangerous', because the effect on prurient minds might be to give them food for their morbid fancies. It is just such a fear which has been largely responsible for the silence and mystery which have for so long been wrapped round the sacred rites of mating.

The question now is, Has this reticence been carried too far? Has it been carried so far that it now tends to defeat its purpose of safeguarding public morals? There are many who unhesitatingly answer such questions in the affirmative. Their intimate knowledge of human lives compels them to recognise that at least as much harm is done by silence as by speaking out. Everything depends on how the matter is presented.

Those who are shocked at the publication of such a book as this on the ground that it gives material for impure minds to sport with, need only reflect that such material is already amply provided in certain comic papers, in hosts of inferior novels, too often on the stage and film, and presented thus in coarse and demoralising guise. It can do nothing but good to such minds to meet the facts they are already so familiar with in a totally new light.

On the other hand, there are all the earnest and noble young minds who seek to know what responsibilities they are taking on themselves when they marry, and how they may best meet these responsibilities. How few of them have more than the vaguest ideas on the subject! How few of them know how or where to obtain the help they desire!

They recoil from the coarse and impure sources of information which are so accessible, and they hesitate to approach those they have learned to regard as virtuous and modest, realising that from such they will receive so little actual information, and that so veiled as to be almost useless.

Dr Stopes has attempted to meet the need of such seekers, and her book will certainly be warmly welcomed by them. It is calculated to prevent many of those mistakes which wreck the happiness of countless lovers as soon as they are actually married. If it did no more than this it would be valuable indeed!

But there is an even more important aspect to be considered – the effect on the child. In all civilised lands there is a growing sense of responsibility towards the young.

The problems of their physical and mental nurture attract more and more attention day by day. Eugenists, educationists, physicians, politicians, philanthropists, and even ordinary parents discuss and ponder, ponder and discuss matters both great and small which have a bearing on the development of the child. By common consent the first seven years of life are regarded as the most critical. It is during these years that the foundations of the personality-to-be are laid – 'well and truly' or otherwise. It is during these years that the deepest and most ineradicable impressions are made in the plastic constitution of the child, arresting or developing this or the other instinctive trend and fixing it, often for life.

And it is during these years above all that the parents play the most important rôle in the inner history of the child's life, not so much by anything they directly teach through verbal exhortations, warnings, or commands, as by those subtler influences which are conveyed in gesture, tone, and facial expression. The younger the child, the more is it influenced through these more primitive modes of expression, and quite as much when they are not directed towards itself but are employed by the parents in their intimate relations with one another in the presence of their apparently unobserving child – the infant in its cot, the toddling baby by the hearth, the little child to all appearance absorbed in its picture book or toy.

Is it not of the utmost importance that these earliest impressions should be of the finest nature? And should we not therefore welcome all that may help – as this book can – to make the living cradle of the next generation as full of beauty and harmony as love and mutual understanding can?

The age-long conflict between the 'lower' and the 'higher' impulses, between the primitive animal nature and the specifically human developments of an altruistic and ethical order, are fought afresh in each soul and in every marriage.

We need to realise more clearly that the lower is never – ought never to be – *eliminated* but rather *subsumed by the higher*. No true harmony can be hoped for so long as one factor or the other is ignored or repressed.

Dr Stopes makes some very important biological suggestions which should not be lightly dismissed. Further observation is required to establish or disprove her theory of the normal sexual cycle in women, but my own observation certainly tends to confirm it.

J. M. MURRAY

Letter

from Professor E. H. Starling, md, bs, frs
Professor of Physiology, University of London

University College
Gower Street, London WC
November 23, 1917

Dear Dr Stopes,

The need of such guidance as you give is very evident. After all, instinct in man is all insufficient to determine social behaviour, and there is need of instruction in the highest of physiological functions, that of reproduction, as there is in the lower functions of eating and drinking – the only difference being that in the former instruction can be deferred to a later age. And there is no doubt that in this case it is better to acquire knowledge by instruction than by a type of experience which is nearly always sordid and may be fraught with danger to the health of the individual and of the family.

At the present time it is of vital importance to the State that its marriages should be fruitful – in children, happiness, and efficiency (and all three are closely connected).

If your book helps in securing this object, your trouble will not have been in vain.

Believe me,

Yours very truly,

ERNEST H. STARLING

Author's Preface

More than ever today are happy homes needed. It is my hope that this book may serve the State by adding to their numbers. Its object is to increase the joys of marriage, and to show how much sorrow may be avoided.

The only secure basis for a present-day State is the welding of its units in marriage; but there is rottenness and danger at the foundations of the State if many of the marriages are unhappy. Today, particularly in the middle classes in this country, marriage is far less really happy than its surface appears. Too many who marry expecting joy are bitterly disappointed; and the demand for 'freedom' grows; while those who cry aloud are generally unaware that it is more likely to have been their own ignorance than the 'marriage-bond' which was the origin of their unhappiness.

It is never *easy* to make marriage a lovely thing; and it is an achievement beyond the powers of the selfish, or the mentally cowardly. Knowledge is needed and, as things are at present, knowledge is almost unobtainable by those who are most in want of it.

The problems of the sex-life are infinitely complex, and for their solution urgently demand both sympathy and scientific research.

I have some things to say about sex, which, so far as I am aware, have not yet been said, things which seem to be of profound importance to men and women who hope to make their marriages beautiful.

This little book is less a record of a research than an attempt to present in easily understandable form the clarified and crystallised results of long and complex investigations. Its simple statements are based on a very large number of first-hand observations, on confidences from men and women of all classes and types, and on facts gleaned from wide reading.

My original contributions to the age-long problems of marriage will principally be found in Chapters IV, V, and VIII. The other chapters fill in what I hope is an undistorted picture of the potential beauties and realities of marriage.

The whole is written simply, and for the ordinary untrained reader, though it embodies some observations which will be new even to those who have made scientific researches on the subjects of sex and human physiology. These observations I intend to supplement and publish at greater length and in more scientific language in another place.

I do not now touch upon the many human variations and abnormalities which bulk so largely in most books on sex, nor do I deal with the many problems raised by incurably unhappy marriages.

In the following pages I speak to those – and in spite of all our neurotic literature and plays they are in the great majority – who are nearly normal, and who are married or about to be married, and hope, but do not know how, to make their marriages beautiful and happy.

To the reticent, as to the conventional, it may seem a presumption or a superfluity to speak of the details of the most complex of all our functions. They ask: Is not instinct enough? The answer is No. Instinct is *not* enough. In every other human activity it has been realised that training, the handing on of tradition are essential. As Dr Saleeby once wisely pointed out: A cat knows how to manage her new-born kittens, how to bring them up and teach them; a human mother does not know how to manage her baby unless she is trained, either directly or by her own quick observation of other mothers. A cat performs her simple duties by instinct; a human mother has to be trained to fulfil her very complex ones.

The same is true in the subtle realm of sex. In this country, in modern times, the old traditions, the profound primitive knowledge of the needs of both sexes have been lost, and nothing but a muffled confusion of individual gossip disturbs a silence, shamefaced or foul. Here and there, in a family of fine tradition, a youth or maiden may learn some of the mysteries of marriage, but the great majority of people in our country have no glimmering of the supreme human art, the art of love; while in books on advanced Physiology and Medicine the gaps, the omissions, and even the misstatements of bare fact are amazing.

In my own marriage I paid such a terrible price for sex-ignorance that I feel that knowledge gained at such a cost should be placed at the service of humanity. In this little book average, healthy, mating creatures will find the key to the happiness which should be the portion of each. It has already guided some to happiness, and I hope it may save some others years of heartache and blind questioning in the dark.

MARIE CARMICHAEL STOPES

Letter

FROM FATHER STANISLAUS ST JOHN, SJ, CF

114, MOUNT STREET
LONDON W1
December 11, 1917

Dear Dr Stopes,

I have read *Married Love* with deep interest. As a piece of thoughtful, scientific writing I find it admirable throughout, and it seems to me that your theme could not have been treated in more beautiful or more delicate language, or with a truer ring of sympathy for those who, through ignorance or want of thought, make shipwreck of their married happiness.

Your clear exposition of the rhythmic curve of sex-feeling and of the misinterpretation on the part of so many husbands of what they call their wives' contrariness, arising from their ignorance of its existence, should bring happiness to many married couples whose lives are drifting apart through want of knowledge. In the exercise of my ministry I have repeatedly traced the beginnings of the rift to this want of knowledge and consequently of sympathy.

So far we are in complete agreement, but our ways part when you treat of birth control.

You write primarily as a scientist (though a very human scientist), and so you are naturally mainly occupied with the facts and conditions of what I may call our earth-life. I, on the other hand, writing as a Catholic, regard our earth-life as essentially and inseparably connected with an eternal existence which reaches out beyond the grave. I look on this life as utterly meaningless in itself, as a period which is simply and solely a means to an end – Eternity – a period of which all the circumstances of pleasure and pain can only be explained and rightly used in their relation to this Eternity.

Let me take in illustration of my meaning the case you give of the worn-out mother of twelve. The Catholic belief is that the loss of health on her part for a few years of life and the diminished vitality on the part of her later children would be a very small price indeed to pay for an endless happiness on the part of all.

In our belief, then, the destruction of one spermatazoon is not the question, but the deliberate prevention of an eternally happy existence which, in the supposition, might arise from its preservation. Holding, as we do, that the marriage-act is the divinely ordained means by which man offers to God the opportunity of creating an immortal being, we do not believe that he may make use of this means and deliberately frustrate it of its end without doing grave wrong.

You do me the honour of suggesting that I should write a foreword to your book, but any foreword from me could obviously only derive value from my position as a Catholic priest, and that position is in opposition to this part of your work.

I cannot end without thanking you very sincerely for allowing me to read your book. Apart from what, as a Catholic, I object to in it, it contains so much most helpful matter that I feel sure it will bring to many a happiness in married life now wanting through the ignorance and the consequent want of sympathy which you so rightly deplore.

Believe me, dear Dr Stopes,
       Yours very sincerely,

I publish this letter with sincere thanks to Father St John for his permission to use it. – M.C.S.

Reply

TO FATHER ST JOHN, SJ

LEATHERHEAD
December 12, 1917

Dear Father St John,

Your letter wins my heart entirely by its appreciation and kindness. It is a great help and encouragement to find that we are so far in essential agreement, and that you are so well disposed toward even part of my effort.

But – and I wish I could say it in burning words – it is not because I am chiefly concerned with Time that I wrote Chapter IX, but just because I am so acutely and so persistently conscious that I am dealing with factors of Eternity. *To me today is essentially a part of my Life Everlasting.*

I cannot separate time and eternity, this world and the next, as religious people often seem able to do; to me this body is a tool in the service of (though not completely in the control of) my immortal soul. Now it seems to me that religious people – and even in your letter I fancy I detect the same tendency (forgive me if I am wrong) – are too ready to separate this world and the next, to act unreasonably or cruelly here and to trust to Eternity, or the Hereafter, to put all right. I do not think that is the way God wills us to work out His plans now that He is giving us the knowledge to do better.

Could there be anything more unreasonable or cruel than

to bring into life half a dozen children *doomed from birth* to ill-health, poverty, and almost inevitable crime?

Christ forgave the thief upon the Cross, but He said, 'Woe unto him through whom offences come. It were better for him that a millstone were hanged about his neck and he cast into the sea.' Would Christ approve of deliberately creating a thief by bringing forth a child who was one inevitably through predictable weakness of physique and mentality and an environment of poverty? ('Thief' stands for criminals in general.)

But more, what about others, born dead, born imbecile, thwarted of life by miscarriage, which tear and rend the overburdened mother so that she is forced to neglect the children she has, and her neglect turns them into thieves? The poor, uneducated mother commits this crime through ignorance: it is *we who know* and allow her to remain in ignorance who are really responsible. Is not our withholding God-given knowledge the greatest stumbling-block of offence to these little ones, and shall we not deserve the millstone round our necks?

Were everyone to have all the children physiologically possible (now that infant mortality is so much reduced by science) in a few centuries there would not be standing room on the earth, and nowhere for a blade of grass or an ear of corn to grow between the crowding feet. Is then a Roman Catholic mother, the increases to whose large family get punier and punier, to be privileged to go deliberately with that host of puny children *at the expense of others*, not only through that part of Eternity called Time, but through all Eternity?

But, dear Father St John, it is not my place to preach or to argue with you, especially after your generous kindness and appreciation. And, alas! I fully realise that even were I granted the tongues of men and of angels, and I converted you to my thought in this matter, you as a Roman Catholic priest could not uphold a position in opposition to your Church.

Oh, that the Churches would look to Christ's own words instead of to the official Church interpretation of them!

I thank you very sincerely for your kindness to a stranger, and remain, always yours respectfully,

MARIE CARMICHAEL STOPES

CHAPTER I

The Heart's Desire

She gave him comprehension of the meaning of love: a word
in many mouths, not often explained. With her, wound in his
idea of her, he perceived it to signify a new start in our existence, a finer shoot of the tree stoutly planted in good gross
earth; the senses running their live sap, and the minds com-
panioned, and the spirits made one by the whole-natured con-
junction. In sooth, a happy prospect for the sons and daughters
of Earth, divinely indicating more than happiness: the speeding
of us, compact of what we are, between the ascetic rocks and
the sensual whirlpools, to the creation of certain nobler races,
now very dimly imagined.

George Meredith, *Diana of the Crossways*, chap. 37

Every heart desires a mate. For some reason beyond our comprehension, nature has so created us that we are incomplete in
ourselves; neither man nor woman singly can know the joy of
the performance of all the human functions; neither man nor
woman singly can create another human being. This fact, which
is expressed in our outward divergencies of form, influences and
colours the whole of our lives; and there is nothing for which
the innermost spirit of one and all so yearns as for a sense of
union with another soul, and the perfecting of oneself which
such union brings.

In all young people, unless they have inherited depraved or
diseased faculties, the old desire of our race springs up afresh in
its pristine beauty.

With the dreams and bodily changes of adolescence, come to

the youth and maiden the strange and powerful impulses of the racial instinct. The bodily differences of the two, now accentuated, become mystical, alluring, enchanting in their promise. Their differences unite and hold together the man and the woman so that their bodily union is the solid nucleus of an immense fabric of interwoven strands reaching to the uttermost ends of the earth; some lighter than the filmiest cobweb, or than the softest wave of music, iridescent with the colours, not only of the visible rainbow, but of all the invisible glories of the wave-lengths of the soul.

However much he may conceal it under assumed cynicism, worldliness, or self-seeking, the heart of every young man yearns with a great longing for the fulfilment of the beautiful dream of a life-long union with a mate. Each heart knows instinctively that it is only a mate who can give full comprehension of all the potential greatness in the soul, and have tender laughter for all the child-like wonder that lingers so enchantingly even in the white-haired.

The search for a mate is a quest for an understanding heart clothed in a body beautiful, but unlike our own.

In the modern world, those who set out on high endeavours or who consciously separate themselves from the ordinary course of social life, are comparatively few, and it is not to them that I am speaking. The great majority of our citizens — both men and women — after a time of waiting, or of exploring, or of oscillating from one attraction to another, 'settle down' and marry.

Very few are actually so cynical as to marry without the hope of happiness; while most young people, however their words may deny it and however they may conceal their tender hopes by an assumption of cynicism, reveal that they are conscious of entering on a new and glorious state by their radiant looks and the joyous buoyancy of their actions. In the kisses and the hand touch of the betrothed are a zest and exhilaration which stir the blood like wine. The two read poetry, listen entranced to music which echoes the songs of their pulses, and see reflected in each other's eyes the beauty of the world. In the midst of this celestial intoxication they naturally assume that, as they are on the threshold of their lives, so too they are in but the ante-chamber of their experience of spiritual unity.

The more sensitive, the more romantic, and the more idealistic is the young person of either sex, the more his or her soul craves for some kindred soul with whom the whole being can unite. But all have some measure of this desire, even the most prosaic, and we know from innumerable stories of real life that the sternest man of affairs, he who may have worldly success of every sort, may yet, through the lack of a real mate, live with a sense almost as though the limbs of his soul had been amputated. Edward Carpenter has beautifully voiced this longing:

That there should exist one other person in the world towards whom all openness of interchange should establish itself, from whom there should be no concealment; whose body should be as dear to one, in every part, as one's own; with whom there should be no sense of Mine or Thine, in property or possession; into whose mind one's thoughts should naturally flow, as it were to know themselves and to receive a new illumination; and between whom and oneself there should be a spontaneous rebound of sympathy in all the joys and sorrows and experiences of life; such is perhaps one of the dearest wishes of the soul.

Love's Coming of Age

It may chance that someone into whose hands this book falls may protest that he or she has never felt the fundamental yearning to form a part of that trinity which alone is the perfect expression of humanity. If that is so, it is possible that all unconsciously he may be suffering from a real malady – sex anaesthesia. This is the name given to an inherent coldness, which, while it lacks the usual human impulse of tenderness, is generally quite unconscious of its lack. It may even be that the reader's departure from the ordinary ranks of mankind is still more fundamental, in which case, instead of sitting in judgment on the majority, he will do well to read some such book as *The Sexual Question* (English translation 1908) by the famous Professor August Forel, in order that his own nature may be made known to him. He may then discover to which type of our widely various humanity he belongs. He need not read my book, for it is written about, and it is written for, ordinary men and women who, feeling themselves incomplete, yearn for a union that will have power not only to make a fuller and richer thing of their own lives, but which will place them in a position to use their sacred trust as creators of lives to come.

It has happened many times in human history that individuals have not only been able to conquer this natural craving for a mate, but have set up celibacy as a higher ideal. In its most beautiful expression and sublimest manifestations, the celibate ideal has proclaimed a world-wide love, in place of the narrower human love of home and children. Many saints and sages, reformers and dogmatists have modelled their lives on this ideal. But such individuals cannot be taken as the standard of the *race*, for they are out of its main current: they are branches which may flower, but never fruit in a bodily form.

In this world our spirits not only permeate matter but find their only expression through its medium. So long as we are human we must have bodies, and bodies obey chemical and physiological, as well as spiritual laws.

If our race as a whole set out to pursue an ideal which must ultimately eliminate bodies altogether, it is clear that very soon we should find the conditions of our environment so altered that we could no longer speak of the human race.

In the meantime, we *are* human. We each and all live our lives according to laws, some of which we have begun to understand, many of which are completely hidden from us. The most complete human being is he or she who consciously or unconsciously obeys the profound physical laws of our being in such a way that the spirit receives as much help and as little hindrance from the body as possible. A mind and spirit finds its fullest expression thwarted by the misuse, neglect or gross abuse of the body in which it dwells.

By the ignorant or self-indulgent breaking of fundamental laws endless harmonies are dislocated. The modern, small-minded ascetic endeavours to grow spiritually by destroying his physical instincts instead of by using them. But I would proclaim that we are set in the world so to mould matter that it may express our spirits; that it is presumption to profess to fight the immemorial laws of our physical being, and that he who does so loses unconsciously the finest flux in which wondrous new creations take their rise.

To use a homely simile – one might compare two human beings to two bodies charged with electricity of different potentials. Isolated from each other the electric forces within them are invisible, but if they come into the right juxtaposition the force is transmuted, and a spark, a glow of burning light arises between them. Such is love.

From the body of the loved one's simple, sweetly coloured flesh, which our immemorial creature instincts urge us to desire, there springs not only the wonder of a new bodily life, but also the enlargement of the horizon of human sympathy and the glow of spiritual understanding which a solitary soul could never have attained alone.

Many reading this may feel conscious that they have had physical union without such spiritual results, perhaps even without an accession of ordinary happiness. If that is so, it can only be because, consciously or unconsciously, they have broken some of the profound laws which govern the love of man and woman. Only by learning to hold a bow correctly can one draw music from a violin: only by obedience to the laws of the lower plane can one step up to the plane above.

CHAPTER II

The Broken Joy

What shall be done to quiet the heart-cry of the world? How answer the dumb appeal for help we so often divine below eyes that laugh?

Æ in *The Hero in Man*

Dreaming of happiness, feeling that at last they have each found the one who will give eternal understanding and tenderness, the young man and maiden marry.*

At first, in the time generally called the honeymoon, the unaccustomed freedom and the sweetness of the relation often does bring real happiness. How long does it last? Too often a far shorter time than is generally acknowledged.

In the first joy of their union it is hidden from the two young people that they know little or nothing about the fundamental laws of each other's being. Much of the sex-attraction (not only among human beings, but even throughout the whole world of living creatures) depends upon the differences between the two that pair; and probably taking them all unawares, those very differences which drew them together now begin to work their undoing.

But so long as the first illusion that each understands the other is supported by the thrilling delight of ever-fresh discoveries, the

* In this, and in most of the generalisations found in this book, I am speaking of things as they are in Great Britain. While, to a considerable extent, the same is true of America and the Scandinavian countries, it must be remembered all through that I am speaking of the British, and primarily of our educated classes.

sensations lived through are so rapid and so joyous that the lovers do not realise that there is no firm foundation of real mutual knowledge beneath their feet. While even the happiest pair may know of divergencies about religion, politics, social custom, and opinions on things in general, these, with goodwill, patience, and intelligence on either side, can be ultimately adjusted, because in all such things there is a common meeting ground for the two. Human beings, while differing widely about every conceivable subject in such human relations, have at least *thought* about them, threshed them out, and discussed them openly for generations.

But about the much more fundamental and vital problems of sex, there is a lack of knowledge so abysmal and so universal that its mists and shadowy darkness have affected even the few who lead us, and who are prosecuting research in these subjects. And the two young people begin to suffer from fundamental divergencies, before perhaps they realise that such exist, and with little prospect of ever gaining a rational explanation of them.

Nearly all those whose own happiness seems to be dimmed or broken count themselves exceptions, and comfort themselves with the thought of some of their friends, who, they feel sure, have attained the happiness which they themselves have missed.

It is generally supposed that happy people, like happy nations, have no history – they are silent about their own affairs. Those who talk about their marriage are generally those who have missed the happiness they expected. True as this may be in general, it is not permanently and profoundly true, and there are people who are reckoned, and still reckon themselves, happy, but who yet unawares reveal the secret disappointment which clouds their inward peace.

Leaving out of account *'femmes incomprises'* and all the innumerable neurotic, super-sensitive, and slightly abnormal people, it still remains an astonishing and tragic fact that *so* large a proportion of marriages lose their early bloom and are to some extent unhappy.

For years many men and women have confided to me the secrets of their lives; and of all the innumerable marriages of which the inner circumstances are known to me, there are tragically few which approach even humanly attainable joy.

Many of those considered by the world, by the relatives, *even by the loved and loving partner*, to be perfectly happy marriages, are secretly shadowed to the more sensitive of the pair.

Where the bride is, as are so many of our educated girls, composed of virgin sweetness shut in ignorance, the man is often the first to create 'the rift within the lute'; but his suffering begins almost simultaneously with hers. The surface freedom of our women has not materially altered, cannot materially alter, the pristine purity of a girl of our northern race. She generally has not even the capacity to imagine the basic facts of physical marriage, and her bridegroom may shock her without knowing that he was doing so. Then, unconscious of the nature, and even perhaps of the existence of his fault, he is bewildered and pained by her inarticulate pain.

Yet I think, nevertheless, it is true that in the early days of marriage the young man is often even more sensitive, more romantic, more easily pained about all ordinary things, and he enters marriage hoping for an even higher degree of spiritual and bodily unity than does the girl or the woman. But the man is more quickly blunted, more swiftly rendered cynical, and is readier to look upon happiness as a Utopian dream than is his mate.

On the other hand, the woman is slower to realise disappointment, and more often by the sex-life of marriage is of the two the more *profoundly* wounded, with a slow corrosive wound that eats into her very being.

Perfect happiness is a unity composed of a myriad essences;

and this one supreme thing is exposed to the attacks of countless destructive factors.

Were I to touch upon all the possible sources of marital disappointment and unhappiness, this book would expand into a dozen bulky volumes. As I am addressing those who I assume have read, or can read, other books written upon various ramifications of the subject, I will not discuss the themes which have been handled by many writers, nor deal with abnormalities, which fill so large a part of most books on sex.

In the last few years there has been such an awakening to the realisation of the corrosive horror of all aspects of prostitution that there is no need to labour the point that no marriage can be happy where the husband has, in buying another body, sold his own health with his honour, and is tainted with disease.

Nor is it necessary, in speaking to well-meaning, optimistic young couples, to enlarge upon the obvious dangers of drunkenness, self-indulgence, and the cruder forms of selfishness. It is with the subtler infringements of the fundamental laws we have to deal. And the prime tragedy is that, as a rule, the two young people are both unaware of the existence of such decrees. Yet here, as elsewhere in Nature, the law breaker is punished whether he is aware of the existence of the law he breaks or not.

In the state of ignorance which so largely predominates today, the first sign that things are amiss between the two who thought they were entering paradise together, is generally a sense of loneliness, a feeling that the one who was expected to have all in common is outside some experience, some subtle delight, and fails to understand the needs of the loved one. Trivialities are often the first indicators of something which takes its roots unseen in the profoundest depths. The girl may sob for hours over something so trifling that she cannot even put into words its nature, while the young man, thinking that he had set out with his soul's beloved upon an adventure into celestial distances, may find himself apparently up against a barrier in her which appears as incomprehensible as it is frivolous.

Then, so strange is the mystical inter-relation between our bodies, our minds, and our souls, that for crimes committed in ignorance of the dual functions of the married pair, and the laws which harmonise them, the punishments are reaped on planes quite diverse, till new and ever new misunderstandings appear to spring spontaneously from the soil of their mutual contact. Gradually or swiftly each heart begins to hide a sense of boundless isolation. It may be urged that this statement is too sweeping. It is, however, based on innumerable actual lives. I have heard from women whose marriages are looked upon by all as the happiest possible expressions of human felicity, the details of secret pain of which they have allowed their husbands no inkling. Many men will know how they have hidden from their beloved wives a sense of dull disappointment, perhaps at her coldness in the marital embrace, or from the sense that there is in her something elusive which always evades their grasp.

This profound sense of misunderstanding finds readier expression in the cruder and more ordinary natures. The disappointment of the married is expressed not only in innumerable books and plays, but even in comic papers and all our daily gossip.

Now that so many 'movements' are abroad, folk on all sides are emboldened to express the opinion that it is marriage itself which is at fault. Many think that merely by loosening the bonds, and making it possible to start afresh with someone else, their lives would be made harmonious and happy. But often such reformers forget that he or she who knows nothing of the way to make marriage great and beautiful with one partner, is not likely to succeed with another. Only by a reverent study of the Art of Love can the beauty of its expression be realised in linked lives.

And even when once learnt, the Art of Love takes *time* to

practise. As Ellen Key says, 'Love requires peace, lc
dream; it cannot live upon the remnants of our time ai
personality.'

There is no doubt that Love loses, in the haste and busue of
the modern turmoil, not only its charm and graces, but some of
its vital essence. The evil results of the haste which so infests
and poisons us are often felt much more by the woman than by
the man. The over-stimulation of city life tends to 'speed up' the
man's reactions, but to retard hers. To make matters worse,
even for those who have leisure to spend on love-making, the
opportunities for peaceful, romantic dalliance are less today in
a city with its tubes and cinema shows than in woods and gar-
dens where the pulling of rosemary or lavender may be the sweet
excuse for the slow and profound mutual rousing of passion.
Now physical passion, so swiftly stimulated in man, tends to
override all else, and the untutored man seeks but one thing –
the accomplishment of desire. The woman, for it is in her nature
so to do, forgives the crudeness, but sooner or later her love
revolts, probably in secret, and then for ever after, though she
may command an outward tenderness, she has nothing within
but scorn and loathing for the act which should have been a
perpetually recurring entrancement.

So many people are now born and bred in artificial and false surroundings, that
even the elementary fact that the acts of love should be *joyous* is unknown to
them. A distinguished American doctor made this amazing statement: 'I do not
believe mutual pleasure in the sexual act has any particular bearing on the
happiness of life.' (*Amer. Med. Assoc. Rep.* 1900.) This is, perhaps, an extreme
case, yet so many distinguished medical men, gynaecologists and physiologists,
are either in ignorance or error regarding some of the profoundest facts of human
sex-life, that it is not surprising that ordinary young couples, however hopeful,
should break and destroy the joy that might have been their life-long crown.

CHAPTER III

Woman's 'Contrariness'

Oh! for that Being whom I can conceive to be in the world, though I shall not live to prove it. One to whom I might have recourse in all my Humours and Dispositions: in all my Distempers of Mind, visionary Causes of Mortification, and Fairy Dreams of Pleasure. I have been trying to train up a Lady or two for these good offices of Friendship, but hitherto I must not boast of my success.

Herrick

What is the fate of the average man who marries, happily and hopefully, a girl well suited to him? He desires with his whole heart a mutual, life-long happiness. He marries with the intention of fulfilling every injunction given him by father, doctor, and friend. He is considerate in trifles, he speaks no harsh words, he and his bride go about together, walk together, read together, and perhaps, if they are very advanced, even work together. But after a few months, or maybe a few years of marriage they seem to have drifted apart, and he finds her often cold and incomprehensible. Few men will acknowledge this even to their best friends. But each heart knows its own pain.

He may at times laugh, and in the friendliest spirit tease his wife about her contrariness. That is taken by everyone to mean nothing but a playful concealment of his profound love. Probably it is. But gnawing at the very roots of his love is a hateful little worm – the sense that she *is contrary*. He feels that she is at times inexplicably cold; that, sometimes, when he has 'done nothing' she will have tears in her eyes, irrational tears which she cannot explain.

He observes that one week his tender love-making and romantic advances win her to smiles and joyous yielding, and then perhaps a few days later the same, or more impassioned, tenderness on his part is met by coldness or a forced appearance of warmth, which, while he may make no comment upon it, hurts him acutely. And this deep, inexplicable hurt is often the beginning of the end of his love. Men like to feel that they understand their dearest one, and that she is a rational being.

After inexplicable misunderstanding has continued for some time, if the man is of at all a jealous nature he will search his wife's acquaintances for someone whom she may have met, for someone who may momentarily have diverted her attention. For however hard it is for the natural man to believe that anyone could step into *his* shoes, some are ready to seek the explanation of their own ill success in a rival. On some occasion when her coldness puzzles him the man is perhaps conscious that his love, his own desires, are as ardent as they were a few days before; then, knowing so intimately his own heart, he is sure of the steadiness of its love, and he feels acutely the romantic passion to which her beauty stirs him; he remembers perhaps that a few days earlier his ardour had awakened a response in her; therefore, he reaches what appears to him to be the infallible logical deduction — that either there must be some rival or his bride's nature is incomprehensible, contrary, capricious. Both thoughts to madden.

With capriciousness, man in general has little patience. Caprice renders his best efforts null and void. Woman's caprice is, or appears to be, a negation of reason. And as reason is man's most precious and hard-won faculty, the one which has raised mankind from the ranks of the brute creation, he cannot bear to see it apparently flouted.

That his bride should lack logic and sweet reasonableness is a flaw it hurts him to recognise in her. He has to crush the thought down.

It may then happen that the young man, himself pained and bewildered at having pained his bride by the very ardour of his affection, may strive to please her by placing restraint upon himself. He may ask himself: Do not religious and many kinds of moral teachers preach restraint to the man? He reads the books written for the guidance of youth, and finds 'restraint', 'self-control', in general terms (and often irrationally) urged in them all. His next step may then be to curtail the expression of his tender feelings, and to work hard and late in the evenings instead of kissing his bride's fingers and coming to her for sweet communion in the dusk.

And then, if he is at all observant, he may be aggrieved and astonished to find her again wistful or hurt. With the tender longing to *understand*, which is so profound a characteristic in all the best of our young men, he begs, implores, or pets her into telling him some part of the reason for her fresh grievance. He discovers to his amazement that *this* time she is hurt because he had not made those very advances which so recently had repelled her, and had been with such difficulty repressed by his intellectual efforts.

He asks himself in despair: What is a man to do? If he is 'educated', he probably devours all the books on sex he can obtain. But in them he is not likely to find much real guidance. He learns from them that 'restraint' is advised from every point of view, but according to the character of the author he will find that 'restraint' means having the marriage relations with his wife not more than three times a week, or once a month – or never at all except for the procreation of children. He finds no *rational* guidance based on natural law.

According to his temperament then, he may begin to practise 'restraint'.

But it may happen, and indeed it has probably happened in

every marriage once or many times, that the night comes when the man who has heroically practised restraint, accidentally discovers his wife in tears on her solitary pillow.

He seeks for advice indirectly from his friends, perhaps from his doctor. But can his local doctor or his friend tell him more than the chief European authorities on this subject? The famous Professor Forel (*The Sexual Question*, transl. 1908) gives the following advice:

> The reformer, Luther, who was a practical man, laid down the average rule of two or three connections a week in marriage, at the time of highest sexual power. I may say that my numerous observations as a physician have generally confirmed this rule, which seems to me to conform very well to the normal state to which *man** has become gradually adapted during thousands of years. Husbands who would consider this average as an imprescriptable right would, however, make wrong pretensions, for it is quite possible for a normal man to contain himself much longer, and it is his duty to do so, not only when his wife is ill, but also during menstruation and pregnancy.

Many men will not be so considerate as to follow this advice, which represents a high standard of living; but, on the other hand, there are many who are willing to go not only so far, but further than this in their self-suppression in order to attain their heart's desire, the happiness of their mate, and consequently their own life's joy.

However willing they may be to go further, the great question for the man is: Where?

There are innumerable leaders anxious to lead in many differ-

---

* The italics are mine. – M.C.S.

This pronouncement of an exceptionally advanced and broad-minded thinker serves to show how little attention has hitherto been paid to the woman's side of this question, or to ascertaining *her* natural requirements.

ent directions. The young husband may try first one and then the other, and still find his wife unsatisfied, incomprehensible – capricious. Then it may be that, disheartened, he tires, and she sinks into the dull apathy of acquiescence in her 'wifely duty'. He is left with an echo of resentment in his heart. If only she had not been so capricious, they would still have been happy, he fancies.

Many writers, novelists, poets and dramatists have represented the uttermost tragedy of human life as due to the incomprehensible contrariness of the feminine nature. The kindly ones smile, perhaps a little patronisingly, and tell us that women are more instinctive, more child-like, less reasonable than men. The bitter ones sneer or reproach or laugh at this in women they do not understand, and which, baffling *their* intellect, appears to them to be irrational folly.

It seems strange that those who search for natural law in every province of our universe should have neglected the most vital subject, the one which concerns us all infinitely more than the naming of planets or the collecting of insects. Woman is *not* essentially capricious; some of the laws of her being might have been discovered long ago had the existence of law been suspected. But it has suited the general structure of society much better for men to shrug their shoulders and smile at women as irrational and capricious creatures, to be courted when it suited them, not to be studied.

Vaguely, perhaps, men have realised that much of the charm of life lies in the sex-*differences* between men and women; so they have snatched at the easy theory that women differ from themselves by being capricious. Moreover, by attributing to mere caprice the coldness which at times comes over the most ardent woman, man was unconsciously justifying himself for at any time coercing her to suit himself.

Circumstances have so contrived that hitherto the explorers and scientific investigators, the historians and statisticians, the poets and artists have been mainly men. Consequently woman's side of the joint life has found little or no expression. Woman has been content to mould herself to the shape desired by man wherever possible, and she has stifled her natural feelings and her own deep thoughts as they welled up.

Most women have never realised intellectually, but many have been dimly half-conscious, that woman's nature is set to rhythms over which man has no more control than he has over the tides of the sea. While the ocean can subdue and dominate man and laugh at his attempted restrictions, woman has bowed to man's desire over her body, and, regardless of its pulses, he approaches her or not as is his will. Some of her rhythms defy him – the moon-months of bearing the growing child and its birth at the end of the tenth wave – these are essentials too strong to be mastered by man. But the subtler ebb and flow of woman's sex has escaped man's observation or his care.

If a swimmer comes to a sandy beach when the tide is out and the waves have receded, leaving sand where he had expected deep blue water – does he, baulked of his bathe, angrily call the sea 'capricious'?

But the tenderest bridegroom finds only caprice in his wife's coldness when she yields her sacrificial body while her sex-tide is at the ebb.

There is another side to this problem, one perhaps even less considered by society. There is the tragic figure of the loving woman whose love-tide is at the highest, and whose husband does not recognise the delicate signs of her ardour. In our anaemic, artificial days it often happens that the man's desire is a surface need, quickly satisfied, colourless, and lacking beauty, and that he has no knowledge of the rich complexities of love-making which an initiate of love's mysteries enjoys. To such a man his wife may indeed seem petulant, capricious, or resentful without reason.

Welling up in her are the wonderful tides, scented and enriched by the myriad experiences of the human race from its ancient days of leisure and flower-wreathed love-making, urging her to transports and to self-expressions, were the man but ready to take the first step in the initiative or to recognise and welcome it in her. Seldom dare any woman, still more seldom dare a wife, risk the blow at her heart which would be given were she to offer charming love-play to which the man did not respond. To the initiate she will be able to reveal that the tide is up by a hundred subtle signs, upon which he will seize with delight. But if her husband is blind to them there is for her nothing but silence, self-suppression, and their inevitable sequence of self-scorn, followed by resentment towards the man who places her in such a position of humiliation while talking of his 'love'.

So unaware of the elements of the physiological reactions of women are many modern men that the case of Mrs G. is not exceptional. Her husband was accustomed to pet her and have relations with her frequently, but yet he never took any trouble to arouse in her the necessary preliminary feeling for mutual union. She had married as a very ignorant girl, but often vaguely felt a sense of something lacking in her husband's love. Her husband had never kissed her except on the lips and cheek, but once at the crest of the wave of her sex-tide (all unconscious that it was so) she felt a yearning to feel his head, his lips, pressed against her bosom. The sensitive inter-relation between a woman's breasts and the rest of her sex-life is not only a bodily thrill, but there is a world of poetic beauty in the longing of a loving woman for the unconceived child which melts in mists of tenderness toward her lover, the soft touch of whose lips can thus rouse her mingled joy. Because she shyly asked him, Mrs G.'s husband gave her one swift unrepeated kiss upon her bosom. He was so ignorant that he did not know that her husband's lips upon her breast melt a wife to tenderness and are one of a husband's first and surest ways to make her physically ready for complete union. In this way he inhibited her natural desire, and as he never did anything to stir it, she neve⟩ any physical pleasure in their relation. Such prudish or car⟩ husbands, content with their own satisfaction, little know the pent-up aching, or even resentment, which may eat into a wife's heart, and ultimately may affect her whole health.

Often the man is also the victim of the purblind social customs which make sex-knowledge *tabu*.

It has become a tradition of our social life that the ignorance of woman about her own body and that of her future husband is a flower-like innocence. And to such an extreme is this sometimes pushed, that not seldom is a girl married unaware that married life will bring her into physical relations with her husband fundamentally different from those with her brother. When she discovers the true nature of his body, and learns the part she has to play as a wife, she may refuse utterly to agree to her husband's wishes. I know one pair of which the husband, chivalrous and loving, had to wait years before his bride recovered from the shock of the discovery of the meaning of marriage and was able to allow him a natural relation. There have been not a few brides whom the horror of the first night of marriage with a man less considerate has driven to suicide or insanity.

That girls can reach a marriageable age without some knowledge of the realities of marriage would seem incredible were it not a fact. One highly educated lady intimately known to me told me that when she was about eighteen she suffered many months of agonising apprehension that she was about to have a baby because a man had snatched a kiss from her lips at a dance.

When girls so brought up are married it is a *rape* for the husband to insist on his 'marital rights' at once. It will be difficult or impossible for such a bride ever after to experience the joys of sex-union, for such a beginning must imprint upon her consciousness the view that the man's animal nature dominates him.

In a magazine I came across a poem which vividly expresses this peculiarly feminine sorrow:

... To mate with men who have no soul above
   Earth grubbing; who, the bridal night, forsooth,
Killed sparks that rise from instinct fires of life,
   And left us frozen things, alone to fashion
Our souls to dust, masked with the name of wife –
   Long years of youth – love years – the years of passion
Yawning before us. So, shamming to the end,
   All shrivelled by the side of him we wed,
Hoping that peace may riper years attend,
   Mere odalisques are we – well housed, well fed.

                                        Katherine Nelson

Many men who enter marriage sincerely and tenderly may yet
have some previous experience of bought 'love'. It is then not
unlikely that they may fall into the error of explaining their
wife's experiences in terms of the reactions of the prostitute.
They argue that, because the prostitute showed physical excitement and pleasure in union, if the bride or wife does not do so,
then she is 'cold' or 'under-sexed'. They may not realise that
often all the bodily movements which the prostitute makes are
studied and simulated because her client enjoys his climax best
when the woman in his arms simultaneously thrills.

As Forel says (*The Sexual Question*, 1908, Engl. trans.): 'The
company of prostitutes often renders men incapable of understanding feminine psychology, for prostitutes are hardly more
than automata trained for the use of male sensuality. When men
look among these for the sexual psychology of woman they find
only their own mirror.'

Fate is often cruel to men, too. More high-spirited young men
than the world imagines strive for and keep their purity to give
their brides; if such a man then marries a woman who is soiled,
or, on the other hand, one who is so 'pure' and prudish that she
denies him union with her body, his noble achievement seems
bitterly vain. On the other hand, it may be that after years of

fighting with his hot young blood a man has given up and gone now and again for relief to prostitutes, and then later in life has met the woman who is his mate, and whom, after remorse for his soiled past, and after winning her forgiveness for it, he marries. Then, unwittingly, he may make the wife suffer either by interpreting her in the light of the other women or perhaps (though this happens less frequently) by setting her absolutely apart from them. I know of a man who, after a loose life, met a woman whom he reverenced and adored. He married her, but to preserve her 'purity', her difference from the others, he never consummated his marriage with her. She was strangely unhappy, for she loved him passionately and longed for children. She appeared to him to be pining 'capriciously' when she became thin and neurotic.

Perhaps this man might have seen his own behaviour in a truer light had he known that some creatures simply *die* if unmated (see Appendix).

The idea that woman is lowered by sex intercourse is very deeply rooted in our present society. Many sources have contributed to this mistaken idea, not the least powerful being the ascetic ideal of the early Church and the fact that man has *used* woman as his instrument so often regardless of her wishes. Women's education, therefore, and the trend of social feeling, has largely been in the direction of freeing her from this and thus mistakenly encouraging the idea that sex-life is a low, physical, and degrading necessity which a pure woman is above enjoying.

In marriage the husband has used his 'marital right'* of inter-

---

* 'Conjugal Rights', *Notes and Queries*, May 16, 1891, p. 383. 'S. writes from the Probate Registry, Somerset House: "Previous to 1733 legal proceedings were recorded in Latin and the word then used where we now speak of *rights* was *obsequies*. For some time after the substitution of English for Latin the term *rites* was usually, if not invariably adopted; *rights* would appear to be a comparatively modern error."

'Mr T. E. Paget writes: "(*Romeo and Juliet*, Act V, Scene III):

course when *he* wished it. Both law and custom have strengthened the view that he has the right to approach his wife whenever he wishes, and that she has no wishes and no fundamental needs in the matter at all.

That woman has a rhythmic sex-tide which, if its indications were obeyed, would ensure not only her enjoyment, but would explode the myth of her capriciousness, seems not to be suspected. We have studied the wave-lengths of water, of sound, of light; but when will the sons and daughters of men study the sex-tide in woman and learn the laws of her Periodicity of Recurrence of desire?

What cursed foot wanders this way tonight
To cross my obsequies, and true lovers rite?
' "Well may Lord Esher say he has never been able to make out what the phrase 'conjugal rights' means. The origin of the term is now clear, and a blunder, which was first made, perhaps, by a type-setter in the early part of the last century, and never exposed until now, has led to a vast amount of misapprehension. Here, too, is another proof that Shakespeare was exceedingly familiar with 'legal language'." '

CHAPTER IV

The Fundamental Pulse

The judgments of men concerning women are very rarely matters of cold scientific observation, but are coloured both by their own sexual emotions and by their own moral attitude toward the sexual impulse ... [Men's] Statements about the sexual impulses of women often tell us less about women than about the persons who make them.

H. Ellis

By the majority of 'nice' people woman is supposed to have no spontaneous sex impulses. By this I do not mean a sentimental 'falling in love', but a physical, a physiological state of stimulation which arises spontaneously and quite apart from any particular man. It is in truth the *creative* impulse, and is an expression of a high power of vitality. So widespread in our country is the view that it is only depraved women who have such feelings (especially before marriage) that most women would rather die than own that they *do* at times feel a physical yearning indescribable, but as profound as hunger for food. Yet many, many women have shown me the truth of their natures when I have simply and naturally assumed that of course they feel it — being normal women — and have asked them only: *When?* From their replies I have collected facts which are sufficient to overturn many ready-made theories about women.

Some of the ridiculous absurdities which go by the name of science may be illustrated by the statement made by Windscheid in the *Centralblatt für Gynäkologie*: 'In the normal woman, especially of the higher social classes, the sexual instinct is acquired, not inborn; when it is inborn, or awakens by itself, there is *abnormality*. Since women do not know this instinct before marriage, they do not miss it when they have no occasion in life to learn it.' (Ellis transl.)

The negation of this view is expressed in the fable of Hera quoted by Helen Key. Hera sent Iris to earth to seek out three virtuous and perfectly chaste maidens who were unsoiled by any dreams of love. Iris found them, but could not take them back to Olympus, for they had already been sent for to replace the superannuated Furies in the infernal regions.

Nevertheless it is true that the whole education of girls, which so largely consists in the concealment of the essential facts of life from them; and the positive teaching so prevalent that the racial instincts are low and shameful; and also the social condition which places so many women in the position of depending on their husband's will not only for the luxuries but for the necessaries of life, have all tended to inhibit natural sex-impulses in women, and to conceal and distort what remains.

It is also true that in our northern climate women are on the whole naturally less persistently stirred than southerners; and it is further true that with the delaying of maturity, due to our ever-lengthening youth, it often happens that a woman is approaching or even past thirty years before she is awake to the existence of the profoundest calls of her nature. For many years before that, however, the unrealised influence, diffused throughout her very system, has profoundly affected her. It is also true that (partly due to the inhibiting influences of our customs, traditions and social code) women may marry before it wakes, and may remain long after marriage entirely unconscious that it surges subdued within them. For innumerable women, too, the husband's regular habits of intercourse, claiming her both when she would naturally enjoy union and when it is to some degree repugnant to her, have tended to flatten out the billowing curves of the line of her natural desire. One result, apparently little suspected, of using the woman as a passive instrument for man's need has been, in effect, to make her that and nothing more. Those men – and there are many – who complain of the lack of ardour in good wives, are often themselves entirely the cause of it. When a woman is claimed at times when she takes no *natural* pleasure in union, it reduces her vitality, and tends to kill her power of enjoying it when the love season returns.

It is certainly true of women as they have been made by the inhibitions of modern conditions, that most of them are only fully awake to the existence of sex after marriage. As we are human beings, the social, intellectual, spiritual sides of the love-choice have tended to mask the basic physiological aspect of women's sex-life. To find a woman in whom the currents are not all so entangled that the whole is inseparable into factors, is not easy, but I have found that wives (particularly happy wives whose feelings are not complicated by the stimulus of another love) who have been separated from their husbands for some months through professional or business duties – whose husbands, for instance, are abroad – are the women from whom the best and most definitive evidence of a fundamental rhythm of feeling can be obtained. Such women, yearning daily for the tender comradeship and nearness of their husbands, find, in addition, at particular times, an accession of longing for the close physical union of the final sex-act. Many such separated wives feel this; and those I have asked to keep notes of the dates, have, with remarkable unanimity, told me that these times came specially just before and some week or so after the close of menstruation, coming, that is, about every fortnight. It is from such women that I got the first clue to the knowledge of what I call the Law of Periodicity of Recurrence of desire in women.

This law it is possible to represent graphically as a curved line; a succession of crests and hollows as in all wave-lines. Its simplest and most fundamental expression, however, is generally immensely complicated by other stimulations which may bring into it diverse series of waves, or irregular wave-crests. We have all, at some time, watched the regular ripples of the sea breaking against a sand-bank, and noticed that the influx of another current of water may send a second system of waves at right angles to the first, cutting athwart them, so that the two series of waves pass through each other.

Woman is so sensitive and responsive an instrument, and so liable in our modern civilised world to be influenced by innumerable sets of stimuli, that it is perhaps scarcely surprising that the deep, underlying waves of her primitive sex-tides have been obscured, and entangled so that their regular sequence has been masked in the choppy turmoil of her sea, and their existence has been largely unsuspected, and apparently quite unstudied.

For some years I have been making as scientific and detailed a study as possible of this extremely complex problem. Owing to the frank and scientific attitude of a number of women, and the ready and intimate confidence of many more, I have obtained a number of most interesting facts from which I think it is already possible to deduce a generalisation which is illuminating, and may be of great medical and sociological value. A detailed statement of this will be given in a scientific publication, but as it bears very intimately on the subject of the present chapter, a short and simple account of my conclusions must be given here.

It is first necessary to consider several other features of woman's life, however.

The obvious moon-month rhythm in woman, so obvious that it *cannot* be overlooked, has been partially studied in its relation to some of the ordinary functions of her life. Experiments have been made to show its influence on the rate of breathing, the muscular strength, the temperature, the keenness of sight, etc., and these results have even been brought together and pictured in a single curved diagram supposed to show the variability in woman's capacities at the different times in her twenty-eight-day cycle.

But it brings home to one how little original work even in this field has yet been done, that the same identical diagram is repeated from book to book, and in Marshall's *Physiology* it is 'taken from Sellheim', in Havelock Ellis 'from Von Ott', and in other books is re-copied and attributed to still other sources, but it is always the same old diagram.

This diagram is reproduced by one learned authority after another, yet nearly every point on which this curve is based appears to have been disputed.

According to this curve, woman's vitality rises during the few days before menstruation, sinks to its lowest ebb during menstruation and rises shortly after, and then runs nearly level till it begins to rise again before the next menstrual period. This simple curve may or may not be true for woman's temperature, muscular strength, and the other relatively simple things which have been investigated. My work and observations on a large number of women all go to show that this curve does *not* represent the waves of woman's sex-vitality.

The whole subject is so complex and so little studied that it is difficult to enter upon it at all without going into many details which may seem remote or dull to the general reader. Even a question which we must all have asked, and over which we have probably pondered in vain – namely, what is menstruation? – cannot yet be answered. To the lay mind it would seem that this question should be answerable at once by any doctor; but many medical men are still far from being able to reply to it even approximately correctly. (See also Appendix, note 2.)

There are a good many slight variations among us, ranging from a three to a five weeks 'month', but the majority of the women of our race have a moon-month of twenty-eight days, once during which comes the flow of menstruation. If we draw out a chart with succeeding periods of twenty-eight days each, looking on each period as a unit: When in this period is it that a normal healthy woman feels desire or any upwelling of her sex-tides?

The few statements which are made in general medical and physiological literature on the subject of sex feeling in women are generally very guarded and vague. Marshall (*Physiology of Reproduction*, p. 138), for instance, says: 'The period of most acute sexual feeling is generally just after the close of the menstrual period.' Ellis speaks of desire being stronger before and sometimes also after menstruation, and appears to lean to the view that it is natural for desire to coincide with the menstrual flow.

After the most careful inquiries I have come to the conclusion that the general confusion regarding this subject is due partly to the great amount of variation which exists between different individuals, and partly to the fact that very few women have any idea of taking any scientific interest in life, and partly to the fact that the more profound, fundamental rhythm of sex desire which I have come to the conclusion exists or is potential in every normal woman, is covered over or masked by the more superficial and temporary influences due to a great variety of stimuli or inhibitions in modern life. For the present consideration I have tried to disentangle the profound and natural rhythm from the more irregular surface waves.

The chart given opposite may assist in making graphically clear what has been said in these last few pages. It is compounded from a number of individual records, and shows a fair average chart of the rhythmic sequence of superabundance and flagging in woman's sex-vitality. The tops of the wave-crests come with remarkable regularity, so that there are two wave-crests in each twenty-eight-day month. The one comes on the two or three days just *before* menstruation, the other after; but after menstruation has ceased there is a nearly level interval, bringing the next wave-crest to the two or three days which come about eight or

CHART I

Curve showing the Periodicity of Recurrence of natural desire in healthy women. Various causes make slight irregularities in the position, size and duration of the 'wave-crests', but the general rhythmic sequence is apparent.

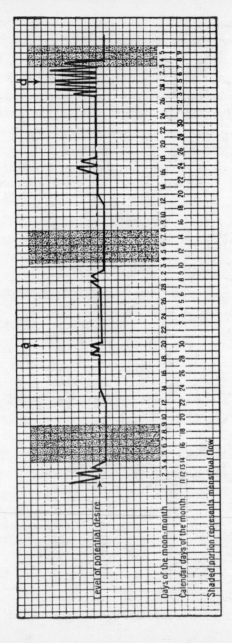

CHART II

Curve showing the depressing effects on the 'wave-crests' of fatigue and over-work. Crest *a* represented only by a feeble and transient up-welling. Shortly before and during the time of the crest *d* Alpine air restored the vitality of the subject. The increased vitality is shown by the height and number of the apices of this wave-crest.

nine days after the close of menstruation – that is, just round the fourteen days, or half the moon-month, since the last wave-crest. If this is put in its simplest way, one may say that there are fortnightly periods of desire, arranged so that one period comes always just *before* each menstrual flow. According to her vitality at the time, and the general health of the woman, the length of each desire-period, or, as we might say, the size and complexity of each wave-crest, depends. Sometimes for the whole of as much as, or even more than three days, she may be ardently and quite naturally stimulated, while at another time the same woman, if she is tired and over-worked, may be conscious of desire for only a few hours, or even less.

The effects of fatigue, city life, bad feeding, and, indeed, of most outward circumstances may be very marked, and may for years, or all her life, so reduce her vitality that a woman may never have experienced any spontaneous sex-impulse at all.

The effects of fatigue, which reduces the vital energy, even in a normal, strongly sexed woman, can be seen in the second curve opposite, where at *a* the intermediate wave-crest is very much reduced. This is not a generalised chart, but a detailed record of an actual individual case.

Curves similar to those shown on page 67 represent in general terms a simplified view of what my research leads me to believe to be the normal, spontaneous sex tide in women of our race. As one young married woman confided to me, her longing for bodily union with her husband, as distinct from her longing for his daily companionship, seemed to well up naturally 'like clockwork', and this when he had been long away from her. But human beings vary remarkably in every particular, and just as no two people have the same features, so no two people would have *absolutely* identical curves were they recorded in sufficient detail. Many a woman is particularly conscious of only one period in each moon-month. Of such women, some feel the period which comes before menstruation, and some feel the one which follows it. In those who generally feel only one, the second period is sometimes felt when they are particularly well, or only when they read exciting novels, or meet the man they love at a time coinciding with the natural, but suppressed, time of desire. There are a few women, who seem to be really a little abnormal, who feel the strongest desire actually during the menstrual flow.

If anyone who reads this thinks to test my view by questioning a number of women, the result will probably appear very conflicting, partly because it is not often that women will tell the truth about such a thing, and partly because in the larger number of women either one or the other period is the more acute and is the one they observe in themselves – if they have observed anything. But a delicate and more accurate investigation of such cases will often bring to light the existence of the second crest of vitality. Once the fundamental idea is grasped, much that appeared obscure or of no significance becomes plain and full of meaning. One lady doctor with whom I discussed my view at once said that it illuminated many observations she had made on her patients, but had not brought together or explained.

There is but little evidence to be found in scientific works on sex, but an interesting instance is mentioned by Forel (*The Sexual Question*, Engl. Transl. page 92) in another connection. He says: 'A married woman confessed to me, when I reproached her for being unfaithful to her husband, that she desired coitus at least once a fortnight, and that when her husband was not there she took the first comer.' Forel did not see any law in this. We may perhaps all see in her want of self-control a grievous *moral* abnormality, but in her fortnightly periods of desire she fits perfectly into the physiological law which, it appears to me, governs the normal sex tides of our race.

In this connection it is of interest to note the decrees of the Mosaic Law regarding marriage intercourse. Not only was all intercourse with a woman during her menstruation period very heavily punished (see Leviticus xx, 18: 'If a man lie with a woman having her sickness ... both of them shall be cut off from among their people'), but the Mosaic Law provided that women should be protected from intercourse for some days *after* each such period. The results obtained by my independent investigation thus find some support in this ancient wisdom of the East. Modern writers are inclined to deride the Mosaic Law on the ground that it prohibits intercourse just at the time when *they think* sex feeling should be strongest. But it does not appear on what grounds they make the latter statement, nor do they give any scientific data in support of it. Thus Galabin in his Manual of Midwifery says: 'In the Jewish law women are directed to abstain* from coitus during menstruation and for seven days after its cessation. Strict observers of the law are said to go beyond what is commanded in Leviticus, and even if discharge lasts only for an hour or two, to observe five days during which the discharge might last, for the period itself, and add to these seven clear days, making twelve in all. It is much to be doubted whether a whole nation was ever induced to practise abstinence at the period of most acute sexual feeling.' But, as will readily be recognised, the old Jewish plan of having twelve clear days after the beginning of menstruation before the next union is in almost exact harmony with the Law of Periodicity of Recurrence of women's desire shown in my charts, pages 67 and 68.

These comparatively simple curves represent what I would postulate as the normal spontaneous up-welling of natural desire in woman. These are the foundations on which the edifice of the physical expression of love may be built. It must not be forgotten, however, that, particularly in modern luxurious life, there are innumerable excitements which may *stimulate* sexual feeling, just as there are many factors in our life which tend to inhibit

---

* Note: In Leviticus xv it is the *man* who is directed to abstain from touching the woman at this period, and who is rendered unclean if he does. – M.C.S.

or retard it. A woman may be, like a man, so swayed by a great love that there is not a day in the whole month when her lover's touch, his voice, the memory of his smile, does not stir her into the thrilling longing for the uttermost union. Hence it is often difficult, particularly for a woman dwelling with the man she loves, to recognise this rhythm in herself, for she may be perpetually stimulated by her love and by his being.

I am convinced, however, that ordinarily, whether she recognises it by outward signs or not, a fortnightly rhythm profoundly influences the average woman, and hence that it fundamentally affects the marriage relation in every way. The burning magnificence of an overpowering life-long love is not given to many, and a husband who desires lasting and mutual happiness in his marriage will carefully study his wife, observe how far she has a normal rhythm, and in what she has little personal traits. He will then endeavour to adapt his demands on her so that they are in harmony with her nature.

This mutual adaptation is not an entirely simple matter, and will be considered in the next chapter.

CHAPTER V

Mutual Adjustment

Love worketh no ill to his neighbour.

St Paul

In the average man of our race desire knows no season beyond the slight slackening of the winter months and the heightening of spring. Some men have observed in themselves a faintly marked monthly rhythm; but in the majority of men desire, even if held in stern check, is merely slumbering. It is always present, ever ready to wake at the lightest call, and often so spontaneously insistent as to require perpetual conscious repression.

It would go ill with the men of our race had woman retained the wild animals' infrequent seasonal rhythm, and with it her inviolable rights in her own body save at the mating season. Woman, too, has acquired a much more frequent rhythm; but, as it does not equal man's, he has tended to ignore and over-ride it, coercing her at all times and seasons, either by force, or by the even more compelling power of 'divine' authority and social tradition.

If man's desire is perpetual and woman's intermittent; if man's desire naturally wells up every day or every few days, and woman's only every fortnight or every month, it may appear at first sight impossible for the unwarped needs of both natures simultaneously to be satisfied.

The sense that a satisfactory mutual adjustment is not within the realms of possibility has, indeed, obsessed our race for centuries. The result has been that the supposed need of one of the partners has tended to become paramount, and we have established the social traditions of a husband's 'rights' and wifely 'duty'. As one man quite frankly said to me: 'As things are it is impossible for both sexes to get what they want. One *must* be sacrificed. And it is better for society that it should be the woman.'

Nevertheless, the men who consciously sacrifice the women are in a minority. Most men act in ignorance. Our code, however, has blindly sacrificed not only the woman, but with her the happiness of the majority of men, who, in total ignorance of its meaning and results, have grown up thinking that women should submit to regularly frequent, or even nightly, intercourse. For the sake of a few moments of physical pleasure they lose realms of ever-expanding joy and tenderness; and while men and women may not realise the existence of an untrodden paradise, they both suffer, if only half consciously, from being shut out from it.

Before making some suggestions which may help married people to find not only a *via media* of mutual endurance, but a *via perfecta* of mutual joy, it is necessary to consider a few points about the actual nature of man's 'desire'. In the innumerable books addressed to the young which I have read, I have not found one which gives certain points regarding the meaning of the male sex-phenomena which must be grasped before it is possible to give rational guidance to intelligent young men. The general ground plan of our physiology is told to us in youth because it so obviously is right for us to know it accurately and in a clean scientific way, rather than to be perpetually perplexed by fantastic imaginings. But the physiology of our most profoundly disturbing functions is ignored – in my opinion, criminally ignored. To describe the essentials, simple, direct and scientific language is necessary, though it may surprise those who are accustomed only to the hazy vagueness which has led to so much misapprehension of the truth. Every mating man and woman should know the following: The sex organs of a man consist not only of the tissues which give rise to the living, moving, ciliated cells, the *sperms*, and of the penis through which they pass and by means of which they are directed into the proper place for their deposition, the woman's vagina. Associated with these primary and essential structures there are other tissues and glands which have numerous subsidiary but yet very important parts to play; some of which influence almost every organ in the body. Man's penis, when unstimulated, is soft, small and drooping. But when stimulated, either by physical touch which acts through the nerves and muscles directly, or indirectly through messages from the brain, it increases greatly in size, and becomes stiff, turgid and erect. Many men imagine that the turgid condition of an erection is due to the local accumulation of sperms, and that these can only be naturally got rid of by an ejaculation. This is entirely wrong. The enlargement of the penis is not at all due to the presence of actual sperm, but is due to the effects of the nervous reaction on the blood-vessels, leading to the filling, principally of the *veins*, and much less of the arteries. As the blood enters but does not leave the penis, the venous cavities in it fill up with venous blood until the whole is rigid. When rigid this organ is able to penetrate the female entrance, and there the further stimulation calls out the sperms from their storehouses, the seminal vesicles in the testes, and they pass down the channel (the urethra) and are expelled. If this is clear, it will be realised that the stiffening and erection does not *necessarily* call for relief in the ejaculation of sperm. If the veins can empty themselves, as they naturally do when the nervous excitement which restricted them locally passes, the erection will subside without any loss of sperms, by the mere passing back of the locally excessive blood into the ordinary circulatory system. This can happen quite naturally and healthily when the nerves are soothed, either physically or as a result of a sense of mental peace and exaltation. When, on the other hand, the local excitement culminates in the calling up and expulsion of the sperms, after it has once started the ejaculation becomes quite involuntary and the sperms and the secretions associated with them pass out of the system and are entirely lost.

Of what does this loss consist? It is estimated that there are somewhere between two and five hundred million sperms in a single average ejaculation.* Each single one of these (in healthy men) is capable of fertilising a woman's egg-cell and giving rise to a new human being. (Thus by a single ejaculation one man might fertilise nearly all the marriageable women in the world!) Each single one of those minute sperms carries countless hereditary traits, and each consists very largely of nuclear plasm – the most highly specialised and richest substance in our bodies. It is not surprising, therefore, to find that the analysis of the chemical nature of the ejaculated fluid reveals among other things a remarkably high percentage of calcium and phosphoric acid – both precious substances in our organisation.

It is therefore the greatest mistake to imagine that the semen is something to be got rid of *frequently* – all the vital energy and the precious chemical substances which go to its composition can be better utilised by being transformed into other creative work on most days of the month. And so mystic and wonderful are the chemical transformations going on in our bodies that the brain can often set this alchemy in motion, particularly if the brain is helped by *knowledge*. A strong will can often calm the nerves which regulate the blood supply, and order the distended veins of the penis to retract and subside without wasting the semen in an ejaculation.

But while it is good that a man should be able to do this often, it is not good to try to do it always. The very restraint which adds to a man's strength up to a point, taxes his strength when

* See Pflügers Archiv., 1891.

carried beyond it. It is my belief that just sufficient restraint to carry him through the ebb-tides of his wife's sex-rhythm is usually the right amount to give the best strength, vigour, and joy to a man if both are normal people. If the wife has, as I think the majority of healthy, well-fed young women will be found to have, a fortnightly consciousness or unconscious *potentiality* of desire, then the two should find a perfect mutual adjustment in having fortnightly unions; for this need not be confined to only a single union on such occasion. Many men, who can well practise restraint for twelve or fourteen days, will find that one union only will not then thoroughly satisfy them; and if they have the good fortune to have healthy wives, they will find that the latter, too, have the desire for several unions in the course of a day or two. If the wave-crests on page 67 are studied, it will be seen that they spread over two or three days and show several small minor crests. This is what happens when a woman is thoroughly well and vital; her desire recurs during a day or two, sometimes even every few hours if it does not, and sometimes even when it does, receive satisfaction.

Expressed in general terms (which, of course, will not fit everybody) my view may be formulated thus: The mutually best regulation of intercourse in marriage is to have three or four days of repeated unions, followed by about ten days without any unions at all, unless some strong external stimulus has stirred a mutual desire.

I have been interested to discover that the people known to me who have accidentally fixed upon this arrangement of their lives are *happy*: and it should be noted that it fits in with the charts I give which represent the normal, spontaneous feeling of so many women.

There are many women, however, who do not feel, or who may not at first recognise, a second, but have only one time of natural pleasure in sex in each moon-month. Many men of strong will and temperate lives will be able so to control themselves that they can adjust themselves to this more restrained sex-life, as do some with whom I am acquainted. On the other hand, there will be many who find this period too long to live through without using a larger amount of energy in restraining their impulse than is justifiable. It seems to me never justifiable to spend so much energy and will power on restraining natural impulses, that valuable work and intellectual power and poise are made to suffer. If, then, a strongly sexed husband, who finds it a real loss to his powers of work to endure through twenty-six days of abstinence, should find himself married to a wife whose vitality is so low that she can only take pleasure in physical union once in her moon-month (in some it will be before, in some a little time after, her menstrual flow), he should note carefully the time she is spontaneously happy in their union, and then at any cost restrain himself through the days immediately following, and about a fortnight after her time of desire he should set himself ardently to woo her. Unless she is actually out of health he is more likely then than at any other time to succeed not only in winning her compliance, but also in giving her the proper feeling and attaining mutual ecstasy.

The husband who so restrains himself, even if it is hard to do it, will generally find that he is a thousand-fold repaid not only by the increasing health and happiness of his wife, and the much intenser pleasure he gains from their mutual intercourse, but also by his own added vitality and sense of self-command. A fortnight is not too long for a healthy man to restrain himself with advantage.

Sir Thomas Clouston says (*Before I Wed*, 1913, page 84): 'Nature has so arranged matters that the more constantly control is exercised the more easy and effective it becomes. It becomes a habit. The less control is exercised the greater tendency there is for a desire to become a *craving* of an uncontrollable kind, which is itself of the nature of disease, and means death sooner or later.' This conclusion is not only the result of the intellectual and moral experience of our race, but is supported by physiological experiments.

While a knowledge of the fundamental laws of our being should in the main regulate our lives, so complex are we, so sensitive to a myriad impressions, that clock-work regularity can never rule us.

Even where the woman is strongly sexed, with a well-marked recurrence of desire, which is generally satisfied by fortnightly unions, it may not infrequently happen that, in between these periods, there may be additional special occasions when there springs up a mutual longing to unite. These will generally depend on some event in the lovers' lives which stirs their emotions; some memory of past passion, such as an anniversary of their wedding, or perhaps will be due to a novel, poem, or picture which moves them deeply. If the man she loves plays the part of tender wooer, even at times when her passion would not *spontaneously* arise, a woman can generally be stirred so fundamentally as to give a passionate return. But at the times of her ebb-tides the stimulus will have to be stronger than at the high tides, and it will then generally be found that the appeal must be made even more through her emotional and spiritual nature and less through the physical than usual.

The supreme law for husbands is: Remember that each act of union must be tenderly wooed for and won, and that no union should ever take place unless the woman also desires it and is made physically ready for it. (See pages 80–1.)

While in most marriages the husband has to restrain himself to meet the wife's less frequently recurrent rhythm, there are, on the other hand, marriages in which the husband is so undersexed that he cannot have ordinary union save at very infrequent intervals without a serious effect on his health. If such a man is married to a woman who has inherited an unusually strong and over-frequent desire, he may suffer by union with her, or may cause her suffering by refusing to unite. It is just possible that for such people the method of Karezza (see Dr A. Stockman's book *Karezza* on the subject) might bring them both the health and peace they need; conserving the man's vital energy from the loss of which he suffers, and giving the woman the sense of union and physical nerve-soothing she requires. But the variations in the sex-needs and the sex-ideas of different healthy people are immense, far greater than can be suggested in this book.

Ellis states that the Queen of Aragon ordained that six times a day was the proper rule in legitimate marriage! So abnormally sexed a woman would today probably succeed in killing by exhaustion a succession of husbands, for the man who could match such a desire is rare, though perhaps less exceptional than such a woman.

Though the timing and the frequency of union are the points about which questions are oftenest asked by the ignorant and well-meaning, and are most misunderstood, yet there are other fundamental facts concerning coitus about which even medical men seem surprisingly ignorant. Regarding these, a simple statement of the physiological facts is essential.

An impersonal and scientific knowledge of the structure of our bodies is the surest safeguard against prurient curiosity and lascivious gloating. This knowledge at the back of the minds of the lovers, though not perhaps remembered as such, may also spare the unintentioned cruelty of handling which so readily injures one whose lover is ignorant.

What actually happens in an act of union should be known. After the preliminaries have mutually roused the pair, the stimulated penis, enlarged and stiffened, is pressed into the woman's vagina. Ordinarily when a woman is not stimulated, the walls of this canal, as well as the exterior lips of soft tissue surrounding it, are dry and rather crinkled, and the vaginal opening is smaller than the man's extended penis. But when the woman is what is physiologically called tumescent (that is, when she is ready for union and has been profoundly stirred) these parts are flushed by the internal blood supply and to some extent are turgid like those of the man, while a secretion of mucus lubricates the channel of the vagina. In an ardent woman the vagina may even spontaneously open and close. (So powerful is the influence of thought on our bodily structure, that in some people all these physical results may be brought about by the thought of the loved one, by the enjoyment of tender words and kisses, and the beautiful subtleties of wooing.) It can therefore be readily imagined that when the man tries to enter a woman whom he has *not* wooed to the point of stimulating her natural physical reactions of preparation, he is endeavouring to force his entry through a dry-walled opening too small for it. He may thus cause the woman actual pain, apart from the mental revolt and loathing she is likely to feel for a man who so regardlessly uses her. On the other hand, in the tumescent woman the opening, already naturally expanded, is lubricated by mucus, and all the nerves and muscles are ready to react and easily accept the man's entering organ. This account is of the meeting of two who have been already married. The first union of a virgin girl differs, of course, from all others, for on that occasion the hymen is broken. One would think that every girl who was about to be married would be told of this necessary rupturing of the membrane and the temporary pain it will cause her; but even still large numbers of girls are allowed to marry in complete and cruel ignorance.

It should be realised that a man does not woo and win a woman once for all when he marries her: *he must woo her before every separate act of coitus*, for each act corresponds to a marriage as other creatures know it. Wild animals are not so foolish as man; a wild animal does not unite with his female without the wooing characteristic of his race, whether by stirring her by a display of his strength in fighting another male, or by exhibiting his beautiful feathers or song. And we must not forget that the wild animals are assisted by nature; they generally only woo just at the season when the female is beginning to feel natural desire. But man, who wants his mate all out of season as well as in it, has a double duty to perform, and must himself rouse, charm, and stimulate her to the local readiness which would have been to some extent naturally prepared for him had he waited till her own desire welled up.

To render a woman ready before uniting with her is not only the merest act of humanity to save her pain, but is of value from the man's point of view, for (unless he is one of those relatively few abnormal and diseased variants who delight only in rape) the man gains an immense increase of sensation from the mutuality thus attained, and the health of both the man and the woman is most beneficially affected.

Assuming now that the two are in the closest mental and spiritual, as well as sensory harmony: in what position should the act be consummated? Men and women, looking into each other's eyes, kissing tenderly on the mouth, with their arms round each other, meet face to face. And that position is symbolic of the coming together of the two who meet together gladly.

It seems incredible that today educated men should be found who – apparently on theological grounds – refuse to countenance any other position. Yet one wife told me that she was crushed and nearly suffocated by her husband, so that it took her hours to recover after each union, but that 'on principle' he refused to attempt any other position than the one he chose to consider normal. Mutual well-being should be the guide for each pair.

It is perhaps not generally realised how great are the variations of size, shape, and position of all the sex parts of the body in different individuals, yet they differ more even than the size and characters of all the features of the face and hands. It happens, therefore, that the position which suits most people is unsatisfactory for others. Some, for instance, can only benefit by union when both are lying on their sides. Though medically this is generally considered unfavourable or prohibitive for conception, yet I know women who have had several children and whose husbands always used this position. In this matter every couple should find out for themselves which of the many possible positions best suits them *both*.

When the two have met and united, the usual result is that, after a longer or shorter interval, the man's mental and physical stimulation reaches a climax in sensory intoxication and in the ejaculation of semen. Where the two are perfectly adjusted, the woman simultaneously reaches the crisis of nervous and muscular reactions very similar to his. This mutual orgasm is extremely important (see also page 85), but in many cases the man's climax comes so swiftly that the woman's reactions are not nearly ready, and she is left without it. Though in some instances the woman may have one or more crises before the man achieves his, it is, perhaps, hardly an exaggeration to say that 70 or 80 per cent of our married women (in the middle classes) are deprived of the full orgasm through the excessive speed of the husband's reactions, or through some maladjustment of the relative shapes and positions of the organs. So deep-seated, so profound, are woman's complex sex-instincts as well as her organs, that in rousing them the man is rousing her whole body and soul. And this takes time. More time, indeed, than the average, uninstructed husband gives to it. Yet woman has at the surface a small vestigial organ called the clitoris, which corresponds morphologically to the man's penis, and which, like it, is extremely sensitive to touch-sensations. This little crest, which lies anteriorly between the inner lips round the vagina, enlarges when the woman is really tumescent, and by the stimulation of movement it is intensely roused and transmits this stimulus to every nerve in her body. But even after a woman's dormant sex-feeling is aroused and all the complex reactions of her being have been set in motion, it may even take as much as from ten to twenty minutes of actual physical union to consummate her feeling, while two or three minutes often completes the union for a man who is ignorant of the need to control his reactions so that both may experience the added benefit of a mutual crisis to love.

A number of well-meaning people demand from men absolute 'continence' save for procreation only. They overlook the innumerable physiological reactions concerned in the act, as well as the subtle spiritual alchemy of it, and propound the view that 'the opposition to continence, save for procreation only, has but one argument to put forward, and that is appetite, selfishness.' (*The Way of God in Marriage.*)

I maintain, however, that it should be realised that the complete act of union is a triple consummation. It symbolises, and at the same time actually enhances, the spiritual union; there are a myriad subtleties of soul-structures which are compounded in this alchemy. At the same time the act gives the most intense physical pleasure and benefit which the body can experience, and it is a *mutual*, not a selfish, pleasure and profit, more calculated than anything else to draw out an unspeakable tenderness and understanding in both partakers of this sacrament; while, thirdly, it is the act which gives rise to a new life by rendering possible the fusion of one of the innumerable male sperms with the female egg-cell.

It often happens nowadays that, dreading the expense and the physical strain of child-bearing for his wife, the husband practises what is called *coitus interruptus* – that is, he withdraws just before the ejaculation, but when he is already so stimulated that the ejaculation has become involuntary. In this way the semen is spent, but, as it does not enter the wife's body, fertilisation and, consequently, procreation cannot take place. This practice, while it may have saved the woman the anguish of bearing unwanted children, is yet very harmful to her, and is to be deprecated. It tends to leave the woman in 'mid-air' as it were; to leave her stimulated and unsatisfied, and therefore it has a very bad effect on her nerves and general health, particularly if it is done frequently. The woman, too, loses the advantage (and I am convinced that it is difficult to overstate the physiological advantage) of the partial absorption of the man's secretions, which must take place through the large tract of internal epithelium with which they come in contact. If, as physiology has already proved is the case, the internal absorption of secretions from the sex organs plays so large a part in determining the health and character of remote parts of the body, it is extremely likely that the highly stimulating secretion of man's semen can and does penetrate and affect the woman's whole organism. Actual experiment has shown that iodine placed in the vagina in solution is so quickly absorbed by the epithelial walls that in an hour it has penetrated the system and is even being excreted. It still remains, however, for scientific experiments to be devised which will enable us to study the effects of the absorption of substances from the semen. On the other hand, *coitus interruptus* is not always harmful for the man, for he has the complete sex-act, though a good many men think its effects on them are undesirable, and it may lead to lack of desire or even impotence toward his wife in a man who practises it with her, or, on the other hand, to a too swift fresh desire from the lack of complete resolution of nervous tension. It is certainly bad when its safety from consequences induces him to frequent indulgence, for thus wastefully to scatter what should be *creative power* is to reduce his own vitality and power of work (see also page 76). By those who have a high appreciation of the value of their creative impulse, and who wish to know the mutual pleasure and enhancement of sex-union without wasting it, this method should not be practised.

It should never be forgotten that without the discipline of control there is no lasting delight in erotic feeling. The fullest delight, even in a purely physical sense, can *only* be attained by those who curb and direct their natural impulses.

Dr Saleeby's words are appropriate in this connection (Introduction to Forel's *Sexual Ethics*, 1908): 'Professor Forel speaks of subduing the sexual instinct. I would rather speak of transmuting it. The direct method of attack is often futile, always necessitous of effort, but it is possible for us to transmute our sex-energy into higher forms in our individual lives, thus justifying the evolutionary and physiological contention that it is the source of the higher activities of man, of moral indignation, and of the "restless energy" which has changed the surface of the earth.'

Forel says (*The Sexual Question*, 1908): 'Before engaging in a life-long union, a man and woman ought to explain to each other their sexual feelings so as to avoid deception and incompatibility later on.' This would be admirable advice were it possible for a virgin girl to know much about the reactions and effects upon her mind and body of the act of coitus, but she does not. Actually it often takes several years for eager and intelligent couples fully to probe themselves and to discover the extent and meaning of the immensely profound physiological and spiritual results of marriage. Yet it is true that a noble frankness would save much misery when, as happens not infrequently, one or other of the pair marry with the secret determination to have no children.

So various are we all as individuals, so complex all the reactions and inter-actions of sex relations, that no hard-and-fast rule can be laid down. Each couple, after marriage, must study themselves, and the lover and the beloved must do what best serves them both and gives them the highest degree of mutual joy and power. There are, however, some laws which should be inviolable. Their details can be gathered from the preceding pages, and they are summed up in the words: 'Love worketh no ill to the beloved.'

CHAPTER VI

Sleep

He giveth His Beloved Sleep.

The healing magic of sleep is known to all. Sleeplessness is a punishment for so many different violations of nature's laws, that it is perhaps one of the most prevalent of humanity's innumerable sufferings. While most of the aspects of sleep and sleeplessness have received much attention from specialists in human physiology, the relation between sleep and coitus appears to be but little realised. Yet there is an intimate, profound and quite direct relation between the power to sleep, naturally and refreshingly, and the harmonious relief of the whole system in the perfected sex-act.

We see this very clearly in ordinary healthy man. If, for some reason, he has to live unsatisfied for some time after the acute stirring of his longing for physical contact with his wife, he tends in the interval to be wakeful, restless, and his nerves are on edge.

Then, when the propitious hour arrives, and after the love-play, the growing passion expands, until the transports of feeling find their ending in the explosive completion of the act, at once the tension of his whole system relaxes, and his muscles fall into gentle, easy attitudes of languorous content, and in a few moments the man is sleeping like a child.

This excellent and refreshing sleep falls like a soft curtain of oblivion and saves the man's consciousness from the jar and disappointment of an anti-climax. But not only is this sleep a restorative after the strenuous efforts of the transport, it has peculiarly refreshing powers, and many men feel that after such a sleep their whole system seems rejuvenated.

But how fare women in this event? When they too have had complete satisfaction they similarly relax and slumber.

But as things are today it is scarcely an exaggeration to say that the majority of wives are left wakeful and nerve-racked to watch with tender motherly brooding, or with bitter and jealous envy, the slumbers of the men who, through ignorance and care-lessness, have neglected to see that they too had the necessary resolution of nervous tension.

Many married women have told me that after they have had relations with their husbands they are restless, either for some hours or for the whole night; and I feel sure that the prevalent failure on the part of many men to effect orgasms for their wives at each congress, must be a very common source of the sleeplessness and nervous diseases of so many married women.

The relation between the completion of the sex act and sleep in woman is well indicated in the case of Mrs A., who is typical of a large class of wives. She married a man with whom she was passionately in love. Neither she nor her husband had ever had connection with anyone else, and, while they were both keen and intelligent people with some knowledge of biology, neither knew anything of the details of human sex union. For several years her husband had unions with her which gave him some satisfaction and left him ready at once to sleep. Neither he nor she knew that women should have an orgasm, and after every union she was left so 'on edge' and sleepless that never less than several hours would elapse before she could sleep at all, and often she remained wakeful the whole night.

After her husband's death her health improved, and in a year or two she entered into a new relation with a man who was aware of women's needs and spent sufficient time and attention to them to ensure a successful completion for her as well as for himself. The result was that she soon became a good sleeper, with the attendant benefits of restored nerves and health.

Sleep is so complex a process, and sleeplessness the resultant of so many different maladjustments, that it is, of course, possible that the woman may sleep well enough, even if she be deprived of the relief and pleasure of perfect union. But in so many married women sleeplessness and a consequent nervous condition are coupled with a lack of the complete sex relation, that one of the first questions a physician *should* put to those of his women patients who are worn and sleepless is: Whether her husband really fulfils his marital duty in their physical relation.

From their published statements, and their admissions to me, it appears that many practising doctors are either almost unaware of the very existence of orgasm in women, or look upon it as a superfluous and accidental phenomenon. Yet to have had a moderate number of orgasms at some time at least is a necessity for the full development of a woman's health and all her powers.

As this book is written for those who are married, I say nothing here about the lives of those who are still unmarried, though, particularly after the age of thirty has been reached, they may be very difficult and need much study and consideration. It is, however, worth noticing how prevalent sleeplessness is among a class of women who have never had any normal sex-life or allowed any relief to their desires. There is little doubt that the complete lack of a normal sex relation is one of the several factors which render many middle-aged unmarried women nervous and sleepless.

Yet for the unmarried woman the lack is not so acute nor so localised as it is for the married woman who is thwarted in the natural completion of her sex-functions after they have been directly stimulated.

The unmarried woman, unless she be in love with some par-

ticular man, has no definite stimulus to her sex desires beyond
the natural upwelling of the creative force. The married woman,
however, is not only diffusely stirred by the presence of the man
she loves, but is also acutely locally and physically stimulated
by his relation with her. And if she is then left in mid-air, without
natural relief to her tension, she is in this respect far worse off
than the unmarried woman.

When a wife is left sleepless through the neglect of the mate
who slumbers healthily by her side, it is not surprising if she
spends the long hours reviewing their mutual position; and the
review cannot yield her much pleasure or satisfaction. For
deprived of the physical delight of mutual orgasm (though, perhaps, like so many wives, quite unconscious of all it can give),
she sees in the sex act an arrangement where pleasure, relief and
subsequent sleep, are all on her husband's side, while she is
merely the passive instrument of his enjoyment. Nay, more than
that: if following every union she has long hours of wakefulness,
she then sees clearly the encroachment on her own health in an
arrangement in which she is not merely passive, but is actively
abused.

Another of the consequences of the incomplete relation is that
often, stirred to a point of wakefulness and vivacity by the preliminary sex-stimulation (of the full meaning of which she may
be unconscious), a romantic and thoughtful woman is then most
able to talk intimately and tenderly – to speak of the things *most*
near and sacred to her heart. And she may then be terribly
wounded by the inattention of her husband, which, coming so
soon after his ardent demonstrations of affection, appears peculiarly callous. It makes him appear to her to be indifferent to the
highest side of marriage – the spiritual and romantic intercourse.
Thus she may see in the man going off to sleep in the midst of
her love-talk, a gross and inattentive brute – and all because she
has never shared the climax of his physical tension, and does
not know that its natural reaction is sleep.

These thoughts are so depressing even to the tenderest and most loving woman, and so bitter to one who has other causes of complaint, that in their turn they act on the whole system and increase the damage done by the mere sleeplessness.

The older school of physiologists dealt in methods too crude to realise the physiological results of our thoughts, but it is now well known that anger and bitterness have experimentally recognisable physiological effects, and are injurious to the whole system.

It requires little imagination to see that after months or years of such embittered sleeplessness, the woman tends not only to become neurasthenic but also resentful towards her husband. She is probably too ignorant and unobservant of her own physiology to realise the full meaning of what is taking place, but she feels vaguely that he is to blame, and that she is being sacrificed for what, in her still greater ignorance of *his* physiology, seems to her to be his mere pleasure and self-indulgence.

He, with his health maintained by the natural outlet followed by recuperative sleep, is not likely to be ready to look into the gloomy and shadowy land of vague reproach and inexplicable trivial wrongs which are all the expression she gives to her unformulated physical grievance. So he is likely to set down any resentment she may show to 'nerves' or 'captiousness'; and to be first solicitous, and then impatient, towards her apparently irrelevant complaints.

If he is, as many men are, tender and considerate, he may try to remedy matters by restricting to the extreme limit of what is absolutely necessary for him, the number of times they come together. Unconsciously he thus only makes matters worse; for as a general rule, he is quite unaware of his wife's rhythm, and does not arrange to coincide with it in his infrequent tender embraces. As he is now probably sleeping in another room and not daring to come for the nightly talks and tenderness which are so sweet a privilege of marriage, here, as in other ways, his well-meaning but wrongly conceived efforts at restraint only tend to drive the pair still further apart.

To make plain the reasonableness of my view regarding sleep, it is necessary to mention some of the immensely profound influences which it is now known that sex exerts, even when not stimulated to its specific use.

In those who are deprived of their sex-organs, particularly when young, many of the other features and organs of the body develop abnormally or fail to appear. Castrated boys (eunuchs) when grown up, tend to have little or no beard, or moustache, to have high-pitched voices and several other characters which separate them from normal men.

The growth of organs and structures so remote from the sex-organs, as, e.g., the larynx, have been found to be influenced by the chemical stimulus of secretions from the sex-organs and their subsidiary glands. These secretions are not passed out through external ducts but enter the blood system *directly*. Such secretions passing straight from the ductless glands into the vascular system are of very great importance in almost all our bodily functions. They have recently been much studied, and the general name of *Hormones* given to them by Starling.* The idea that some particular secretions or 'humours' are connected with each of the internal organs of the body, is a very ancient one; but we have even yet only the vaguest and most elementary knowledge of a few of the many miracles performed by these subtle chemical substances. Thus we know that the stimulus of food in the stomach sends a chemical substance from one ductless gland in the digestive system chasing through the blood to another gland which prepares a different digestive secretion further on. We know that the thyroid gland in the neck swells and contracts in very sensitive relation with the sex organs; we know that some chemical secretion from the developing embryo, or the tissue in

* See Prof. Ernest H. Starling's Croonian Lecture to the Royal Society, 1905.

which it grows, sends its chemical stimulus to the distant mammary glands of the mother; we know that if the ovaries of a girl or the testes of a boy are completely cut out, the far-reaching influences their hormones would have exerted are made evident by the numerous changes in the system and departures from the normal, which result from their lack.

But we do *not* know, for physiologists have not yet studied the degree and character of the immense stimulus of sex-life and experience on the glands of the sex-organs, or how they affect the whole of the human being's life and powers.

The 'Mendelians' and the 'Mutationists', who both tend to lay so much (and I think such undue) stress on morphological hereditary factors, seem at present to have the ear of the public more than the physiologists. But it is most important that every grown up man and woman should know that through the various chemical substances or 'messengers' (which Starling called the hormones) there is an extremely rapid, almost immediate, effect on the activities of organs in remote parts of the body, due to the influences exerted on one or other internal organ.

It is therefore clear that any influences exerted on such profoundly important organs as those connected with sex must have far-reaching results in many unexpected fields.

What must be taking place in the female system as a result of the completed sex act?

It is true that in coitus woman has but a slight external secretion, and that principally of mucus. But we have no external signs of all the complex processes and reactions going on in digestion and during the production of digestive secretions. When, as is the case in orgasm, we have such intense and apparent nervous, vascular and muscular reactions, it seems inevitable that there must be correspondingly profound internal correlations. Is it conceivable that organs so fundamentally placed, and whose mere existence we know affects the personal characters of women, could escape physiological result from the intense preliminary stimulus and acute sensations of an orgasm?

To ask this question is surely to answer it. It is to my mind inconceivable that the orgasm in woman as in man should not have profound physiological effects. Did we know enough about the subject, many of the 'nervous breakdowns' and neurotic tendencies of the modern woman could be directly traced to the partial stimulation of sexual intercourse without its normal completion which is so prevalent in modern marriage.

This subject, and its numerous ramifications, are well worth the careful research of the most highly trained physiologists. There is nothing more profound, or of more vital moment to modern humanity as a whole, than is the understanding of the sex nature and sex needs of men and women.

I may point out as a mere suggestion that the man's sex-organs give rise to *external* and also to *internal* secretions. The former only leave the glands which secrete them as a result of definite stimulus; the latter appear to be perpetually exuded in small quantities and always to be entering and influencing the whole system. In women we know there are corresponding perpetual internal secretions, and it seems evident to me that there must be some internal secretions which are only released under the definite stimulus of the whole sex-act.

The English and American peoples, who lead the world in so many ways, have an almost unprecedentedly high proportion of married women who get no satisfaction from physical union with their husbands, though they bear children, and may in every other respect appear to be happily married.

The modern civilised neurotic woman has become a by-word in the Western world. Why?

I am certain that much of this suffering is caused by the *ignorance* of both men and women regarding not only the inner physiology, but even the obvious outward expression, of the complete sex-act.

Many medical men now recognise that numerous nervous and other diseases are associated with the lack of physiological relief for natural or stimulated sex feelings in women. Ellis* quotes the opinion of an Austrian gynaecologist who said that, 'of every hundred women who come to him with uterine troubles, seventy suffer from congestion of the womb, which he regarded as due to incomplete coitus.' While a writer in a recent number of the *British Medical Journal*† published some cases in which quite serious nervous diseases in wives were put right when their husbands were cured of too hasty ejaculation.

Sleep, concerning which I began this chapter, is but one of innumerable indications of inner processes intimately bound up with the sex-reactions. When the sex-rite is, in every sense, rightly performed, the healing wings of sleep descend both on the man and on the woman in his arms. Every organ in their bodies is influenced and stimulated to play its part, while their spirits, after soaring in the dizzy heights of rapture, are wafted to oblivion, thence to return gently to the ordinary plains of daily consciousness.

* H. Ellis, *Sex in Relation to Society*, 1910, p. 551.
† See Porosz, *British Medical Journal*, April 1, 1911, p. 784.

CHAPTER VII

Modesty and Romance

> A person can therefore no more promise to love or not to love
> than he can promise to live long. What he can promise is to
> take good care of his life and of his love.
>
> Ellen Key

Artists clearly, and poets in veiled language, have in all ages,
expressed the glory of the naked human body. Before the Venus
of Milo in her Paris home, even the empty-headed and ridicu-
lously dressed creatures of fashion stand for a moment with a
catch in the throat and a sense that here is something full of
divine secrets. One day, when I was doing my reverence before
this ancient goddess, drinking in strength and happiness from
the harmonies of her curves, a preposterously corseted doll came
up to the statue, paused, and said with tears in her voice to the
man beside her: 'Hasn't she got the *loveliest* figure!'

If cold marble so stirs us, how much more the warmth and
vitality of living beauty! Any well-formed young man or woman
is immeasurably more graceful when free from the clinging follies
of modern dress, while a beautiful woman's body has a supernal
loveliness at which no words short of a poetic rapture can even
hint. Our race has so long neglected the culture of human beauty
that a sad proportion of mature men and women are unattrac-
tive; but most young people have the elements of beauty, and
to them chiefly this book is addressed.

A young man or woman perfectly naked *cannot* be tawdry.
The fripperies, the jagged curves and inharmonious lines and

colours of the so-called 'adornments' are surmounted, and the naked figure stepping from their scattered pile is seen in its utter simplicity. How charming even the raggedest little street urchins become when they leave their rags on the bank and plunge into the water!

It is therefore not surprising that one of the innumerable sweet impulses of love should be to reveal, each to each, this treasure of living beauty. To give each other the right to enter and enjoy the sight which most of all sights in the world draws and satisfies the artist's eyes.

This impulse, however, is, on the part of the woman, swayed by two at least of the natural results of her rhythmic tides. For some time during each month, age-long tradition that she is 'unclean', coupled with her obvious requirements, have made her withdraw herself from even her husband's gaze. But, on the other hand, there regularly come times when her body is raised to a higher point of loveliness than usual by the rounding and extra fullness of the breasts. (This is one of the regular physiological results of the rhythmic processes going on within her.) Partly or wholly unconscious of the brilliance and full perfection of her beauty, she yet delights in its gentle promptings to reveal itself to her lover's eyes when he adores. This innocent, this goddess-like self-confidence retreats when the natural ebb of her vitality returns.

How fortunate for man when these sweet changes in his lover are not coerced into uniformity! For man has still so much of the ancient hunter in his blood that beauty which is always at hand and ever upon its pedestal must inevitably attract him far less than the elusive and changing charms of rhythmic life. In the highly evolved and cultivated woman, who has wisdom enough not to restrict, but to give full play to the great rhythms of her being, man's polygamous instinct can be satisfied and charmed by the ever-changing aspects of herself which naturally come uppermost. And one of her natural phases is at times to

retreat, to experience a profound sex indifference, and passionately to resent any encroachment on her solitude.

This is something woman too often forgets. She has been so
thoroughly 'domesticated' by man that she feels too readily that
after marriage she is all his. And by her very docility to his
perpetual demands, she destroys for him the elation, the palpitat-
ing thrills and surprises, of the chase.

In the rather trivial terms of our sordid modern life, it works
out in many marriages somewhat as follows: The married pair
share a bedroom, and so it comes about that the two are together
not only at the times of delight and interest in each other, but
during most of the unlovely and even ridiculous proceedings of
the toilet. Now it may enchant a man once – perhaps even twice
– or at long intervals – to watch his goddess screw her hair up
into a tight and unbecoming knot and soap her ears. But it is
inherently too unlovely a proceeding to retain indefinite enchant-
ment. To see a beautiful woman floating in the deep, clear water
of her bath – that may enchant for ever, for it is so lovely, but
the unbeautiful trivialities essential to the daily toilet tend only
to blur the picture and to dull the interest and attention that
should be bestowed on the body of the loved one. Hence, ultimately, everyday association in the commonplace daily necessi-
ties tends to reduce the keen pleasure each takes in the other.
And hence, inevitably and tragically, though stealthily and
unperceived, to reduce the keenness of stimulation the pair exert
on each other, and thus to lower their intensity of the consummation of the sex act, and hence to lower its physiological
value.*

---

* A quotation from Thomas (p. 112 of William Thomas' book *Sex and Society*,
1907, pp. 314) is here very apt, though he had been speaking not of man, but
of the love play and coyness shown by female birds and animals.

  We must also recognise the fact that reproductive life must be connected
  with violent stimulation, or it would be neglected and the species would
  become extinct; and on the other hand, if the conquest of the female were
  too easy, sexual life would be in danger of becoming a play interest and a

In short, the overcoming of her personal modesty, which is generally looked on as an essential result in marriage where the woman becomes wholly the man's, has generated among our women a tradition that before their husbands they can perform any and all of the details of personal and domestic duties. Correspondingly, they allow the man to be neglectful of preserving some reticence before them. This mutual possession of the lower and more elementary experiences of life has been, in innumerable marriages, a factor in destroying the mutual possession of life's higher and more poetic charms.

And woman's beauty wanes too often more through neglect than through age. The man, with the radiant picture of his bride blurred by the daily less lovely aspects, may cease to remind her by acts of courtship that her body is precious. But many men by whom each aspect of their wives is noted, are often hurt by woman's stupidity or neglect of herself. Women lose their grace of motion by relying on artificial bones and stiffenings, and clog their movements with heavy and absurdly fashioned garments. They forget how immeasurably they can control not only their clothed appearance but the very structure of their bodies by the things they eat and do, by the very thoughts they think.

A wise man once said that a woman deserved no credit for her beauty at sixteen, but beauty at sixty was her own soul's doing. I would that all the world so thirsted for beauty that we moulded the whole race into as lovely forms as the Greeks created.

dissipation, destructive of energy and fatal to the species. Working, we may assume, by a process of selection and survival, nature has both secured and safeguarded reproduction. The female will not submit to seizure except in a high state of nervous excitation (as is seen especially well in the wooing of birds), while the male must conduct himself in such a way as to manipulate the female; and, as the more active agent, he develops a marvellous display of technique for this purpose. This is offset by the coyness and coquetry of the female, by which she equally attracts and fascinates the male, and practises upon him to induce a corresponding state of nervous excitation.

In this respect I am inclined to think that man suffers more than woman. For man is still essentially the hunter, the one who experiences the desires and thrills of the chase, and dreams ever of coming unawares upon Diana in the woodlands. On the other hand, the married woman, having once yielded all, tends to remain passively in the man's companionship.

Though it may appear trivial beside the profound physiological factors considered in recent chapters, I think that, in the interests of husbands, an important piece of advice to wives is: Be always escaping. Escape the lower, the trivial, the sordid. So far as possible (and this is far more possible than appears at first, and requires only a little care and rearrangement in the habits of the household) ensure that you allow your husband to come upon you only when there is delight in the meeting. Whenever the finances allow, the husband and wife should have separate bedrooms. No soul can grow to its full stature without spells of solitude. A married woman's body and soul should be essentially her own, and that can only be so if she has an inviolable retreat. But at the same time the custom of having separate rooms should not mean, as it often does, that the husband only comes to his wife's room when he has some demand to make upon her. Nothing is more calculated to inhibit all desire for union in a sensitive wife than the knowledge of what her husband wants when he comes, however lovingly, to her side. Every night, unless something prevents, there should be the tender companionship and whispered intimacies which are, to many people, only possible in the dark. The 'good-night' should be a time of delightful forgetting of the outward scars of the years, and a warm, tender, perhaps playful exchange of confidences. This is not incompatible with what has been said in the previous chapters, and when this custom is maintained it overcomes the objection some people make to separate rooms as a source of estrangements.

CHAPTER VIII

Abstinence

How intoxicating indeed, how penetrating – like a most precious wine – is that love which is the sexual transformed by the magic of the will into the emotional and spiritual! And what a loss on the merest grounds of prudence and the economy of pleasure is its unbridled waste along physical channels! So nothing is so much to be dreaded between lovers as just this – the vulgarisation of love – and this is the rock upon which marriage so often splits.

Edward Carpenter

And because marriage so often splits upon this rock, or because men and women have in all ages yearned for spiritual beauty, there have been those who shut themselves off from all the sweet usages of the body. In the struggle of man to gain command over his body, and in the slow and often backsliding evolution of the higher love, there is no doubt that humanity owes much to the ascetic. But this debt is in the past. We are now gaining control of the lower forces, we are winning knowledge of the complex meanings and the spiritual transformations of our physical reactions, and in the *future* the highest social unit will be recognised to be the pair, fused in love so that all human potentialities are theirs, as well as the higher potentialities which only perfect love can originate.

Yet, as we live today, with still so many remnants of the older standards within and upon us, we must endeavour to understand the ascetic. He (less often she) is by no means seldom one of the products of marriage. It not infrequently happens that after a love-marriage and some years of what is considered happiness, the man or woman may withdraw from the sex-life, often looking down upon it, and considering that they have reached a higher plane by so doing. But such people seldom ask themselves if, while they lived it, they reached the highest possible level of the sex-life.

One of the most famous instances of the married ascetic is Tolstoy, whose later opinion was that the *highest* human being completely inhibits his sex-desires and lives a celibate life. Ascetics, however, seldom have much knowledge of human physiology, and it seems to me that, with all their fine and religious fervour, they often lack the mysticism necessary for the full realisation of the meaning and potentialities of the new creation resulting from man's and woman's highest union. Doubtless if for an hour we were to take the place of the individual chemical atoms of Oxygen or of Hydrogen, we could have no inkling of the physical properties of the water-drop they together form.

Christianity, like most religions, had a strong wave of asceticism early in its history. While there was, as there still is, a harsh asceticism which is hostile to the other sex, it is of much interest to see that there was also a romantic asceticism which, while revolting from the sensuality of the pagan contemporaries, did not entirely prohibit the charms and pleasures of mutual companionship. Thus, in a mutilated form, it seems these early Christian ascetics gained some of the immaterial benefits of marriage. Ellis (Vol. 6, *Sex and Society*, 1913) gives an interesting account of these ascetic love-unions:

'Our fathers,' Chrysostom begins (*Against those who keep Virgins in their Houses*), 'only knew two forms of sexual intimacy, marriage and fornication. Now a third form has appeared: men introduce young girls into their houses and keep them there permanently, respecting their virginity. What,' Chrysostom asks, 'is the reason? It seems to me that life in common with a woman is sweet, even outside conjugal union and fleshly commerce. That is my feeling; and perhaps it is not my feeling alone; it may also be that of these men. They would not hold their honour so cheap nor give rise to such scandals if this pleasure were not violent and tyrannical ... That there should really be a pleasure in this which produces a love more ardent than conjugal union may surprise you at first. But when I give you the proofs you will agree that it is so.' The absence of restraint to desire in marriage, he continues, often leads to speedy disgust, and even apart from this, sexual intercourse, pregnancy, delivery, lactation, the bringing up of children, and all the pains and anxieties that accompany these things, soon destroy youth and dull the point of pleasure. The virgin is free from these burdens. She retains her vigour and her youthfulness, and even at the age of forty may rival the young nubile girl. 'A double ardour thus burns in the heart of him who lives with her, and the gratification of desire never extinguishes the bright flame which ever continues to increase in strength.' Chrysostom describes minutely all the little cares and attentions which the modern girls of his time required, and which these men delighted to expend on their virginal sweethearts whether in public or in private. He cannot help thinking, however, that the man who lavishes kisses and caresses on a woman whose virginity he retains is putting himself somewhat in the position of Tantalus. But this new refinement of tender chastity, which came as a delicious discovery to the early Christians who resolutely thrust away the licentiousness of the pagan world, was deeply rooted, as we discover from the frequency with which the grave Fathers of the Church, apprehensive of scandal, felt called upon to reprove it, though their condemnation is sometimes not without a trace of secret sympathy.

Thus Jerome, in his letter to Eustochium, refers to those couples who 'share the same room', often even the same bed, and call us suspicious if we draw any conclusions; while Cyprian (*Epistola*, 86) is unable to approve of those men he hears of, one a deacon, who live in familiar intercourse with virgins, even sleeping in the same bed with them, for, he declares, the feminine sex is weak and youth is wanton.

The harsh ascetic, however, is the one the word ascetic most generally conjures up. Even if he accomplishes miracles of self-restraint, and subdues desire, he is often weakened rather than strengthened by his determination to flout nature. Save only in the truly great, there is a warping and narrowing which results from coercing beyond the limits of reason the desires which were implanted in Adam and Eve when they were told to be fruitful and multiply.

As Ellen Key says (*Love and Marriage*):

Those ascetics who recommend only self-control as a remedy for the mastery of sexual instinct, even when such control becomes merely obstructive to life, are like the physician who tried only to drive the fever out of his patient: it was nothing to him that the sick man died of the cure.

But these ascetics may have arrived at their fanaticism by two different paths. One group – which includes most of the female ascetics – hates Cupid because he has never shown to them any favour. The other group – embracing the majority of male ascetics – curse him because he never leaves them in peace.

Approaching the subject in a more modern and scientific attitude of impartial inquiry, the medical man can produce an imposing list of diseases more or less directly caused by abstinence both in men and in women. These diseases range from neuralgia and 'nerves' to (in women) fibroid growths. And it is well worthy of remark that these diseases may be present when the patient (as have many unmarried women) has no idea that the sex-impulse exists unmastered.

Thus the ascetic and the profligate (whether or not in *legal* marriage) have both to run the gauntlet of disease. There is, however, no disease I know of which is caused by the normal and mutually happy marriage relation – a relation which, certainly to most, has positive healing and vitalising power.

The profound truth which is perceived by the ascetics is that the creative energy of sex can be *transformed* into other activities. This truth should never be lost sight of in marriage; where between the times of natural, happy, and also stimulating exercise of the sex-functions, the periods of complete abstinence should be opportunities for transmuting the healthy sex-power into work of every sort.

CHAPTER IX

Children

I am for you, and you are for me,
Not only for your own sake, but for others' sakes,
Envelop'd in you sleep greater heroes and bards,
They refuse to awake at the touch of any man but me.
                                        Walt Whitman

The Mystic in his moment of enlightenment attains through the flux of his personality the realisation of oneness with the divine forces of the Universe.

To ordinary men and women, however, this mystical ecstasy is unknown, and the ordinary human consciousness is far more aware of its separateness than of its oneness with the vital forces of creation. Yet the glow of half swooning rapture in which the mystic's whole being melts and floats in the light of the divine force is paralleled in the rapture of lovers.

When two who are mated in every respect burn with the fire of the innumerable forces within them, which set their bodies longing towards each other with the desire to inter-penetrate and to encompass one another, the fusion of joy and rapture is not purely physical. The half swooning sense of flux which overtakes the spirit in that eternal moment at the apex of rapture sweeps into its flaming tides the whole essence of the man and woman, and as it were, the heat of the contact vapourises their consciousness so that it fills the whole of cosmic space. For the moment they are identified with the divine thoughts, the waves of eternal force, which to the Mystic often appear in terms of golden light.

From their mutual penetration into the realms of supreme joy the two lovers bring back with them a spark of that light which we call life.

And unto them a child is born.

This is the supreme purpose of nature in all her enticing weft of complex factors luring the two lovers into each other's arms. Only by the fusion of two can the new human life come into being, and only by creating a new life in this way can we hand on the torch which lights our consciousness in the sphere of matter.

This mystical and wonderful fact has never yet found the poet to sing its full glory. But in the hearts of all who have known true love lies the realisation of the sacredness that is theirs when they are in the very act of creation.

Were our bodies specifically organised for this supreme purpose, two human beings would only pass through the sacred fire of mutual fusion in order to create a new life. But, however far our spirits have evolved, our bodies are composed of matter which bears the imprint of the many past phases through which we have reached our present position. And because in the world of the lower animals there is an immense wastage of all the young lives created, and it is necessary that myriads should be conceived in order that a small number should reach maturity, so in our bodies (specialised though they are in comparison with the lower animals) both sexes still produce a far larger number of germs awaiting fertilisation than can be actually fructified and imbued with individual life. So profoundly has the course of our history been stamped upon us that each germ, unaware of its own futility if it reaches maturity at an unpropitious moment is just as insistent in its development as the favoured one which follows out the full natural course of its career and gives rise to a new individual.

It is utterly impossible, organised as our bodies are at present, for us to obey the dictates of theologians and refrain from the destruction of potential life. The germ cells of the woman, though immeasurably less numerous than the male germ cells (the sperm) yet develop uselessly over and over again in every celibate as well as in every married woman. While myriads of sperm cells are destroyed even in the process of the act which does ensure fertilisation of the woman by the single favoured sperm. If the theologians really mean what they say, and demand the voluntary effort of complete celibacy from all men, save for the purpose of procreation, this will *not* achieve their end of preventing the destruction of all potential life; and the monthly loss of unfertilised eggcell by women is beyond all the efforts of the will to curb. Nature, not man, arranged the destruction of potential life against which ascetic Bishops rage.

If, then, throughout the greater part of their lives the germinal cells of both sexes inevitably disintegrate without creating an embryo, there can be nothing wrong in selecting the most favourable moment possible for the conception of the first of these germinal cells to be endowed with the supreme privilege of creating a new life.

What generally happens in marriage where this is not thought of is that one of the very earliest unions results in the fertilisation of the wife, so that the young pair have a baby nine months, or a little more, after marriage.

Whereas, were they wise and did they realise the full significance of what they were doing, they would allow at least six months or a year to elapse before beginning the supreme task of their lives, the burden of which falls mainly upon the woman.

For many reasons it is more ideal to have the children spontaneously and early; but if economic conditions are hard, as they so often are in 'civilised' life, it may be better to marry and defer the children rather than not to marry.

If the pair married very young, and before they could afford to support children, they might wait several years with advantage. An exceptional case is one of the happiest marriages I know. The pair married while they were young students in the University, and fourteen years later they had their first child, a splendidly healthy boy. Though such a long interval is certainly not to be universally recommended, as it is said that it may result in sterility, in this instance it was triumphantly better for the two to have lived normally satisfied happy lives than to have waited for fourteen years and risked the man's 'fall'.

There are many reasons, both for their own and for the child's sake, why the potential parents should take the wise precaution of delay, unless owing to special circumstances they cannot expect to live together uninterruptedly.

The child, conceived in rapture and hope, should be given every material chance which the wisdom and love of the parents can devise. And the first and *most* vital condition of its health is that the mother should be well and happy and free from anxiety while she bears it.

The tremendous and far-reaching effects of marriage on the woman's whole organism make her less fitted to bear a child at the very commencement of marriage than later on, when the system will have adjusted itself to its new conditions.

Not only for the sake of the child, however, should the first conception be a little delayed, but also to secure the lasting happiness of the married lovers. It is generally (though perhaps not always) wise thoroughly to establish their relation to each other before introducing the inevitable dislocation and readjustment necessitated by the wife's pregnancy and the birth of a child.

In this book I am not speaking so much of the universal sex relation as to those who find themselves today in the highly civilised, artificial communities of English-speaking people: and in our present society there is little doubt that the early birth of a child demands much self-sacrifice and self-restraint from the man, one of the reflex vibrations of which is his undefinable sense of loss and separation from his bride. This has been confided to me by many men who have been generous enough to trust me with some of the secrets of their lives. Mr C. is typical of many others of his class.

He was quiet and refined, with a strong strain of romantic love, which was entirely centred in his bride. He was manly and sufficiently virile to feel the need of sex intercourse, but he was unaware (as are so many men) of the woman's corresponding need; and he did not give his wife any orgasm. She took no pleasure, therefore, in the physical act of union, which for her was so incomplete.

Very shortly after marriage she conceived, and a child was born ten months after the wedding day.

For two years after the birth of the child her vitality was so lowered that the sex-act was to her *so* repugnant that she refused her husband any union; and it was thus three years after their marriage before they met in anything like a normal way. By that time the long separation from sex-life, and the strain on the man, coupled with daily familiarity at home, had dimmed, if not completely destroyed, his sense of romance. The natural stimulation each should exert on the other had faded, so that they never experienced the mutual glow of rapture in their sex-union.

Another pair suffered similarly: Mr and Mrs D. were prevented for several years by the wife's real and fancied ill-health from having any intercourse. When, after that time, she recovered and passionately desired the true marriage relation, the husband felt it to be impossible. To him it would have been, as he expressed it, 'like raping his sister'.

Once such a thought has grown into a man's mind it is very difficult 'to recapture the first fine early rapture'. And with the loss of that early rapture the two lose, for the rest of their lives, the irradiating joy which is priceless not only for its beauty, but for the vitality with which its wings are laden.

On the other hand, if by waiting some months (or even years if they are young) the mated pair have learnt to adjust themselves to each other and have experienced the full possibilities of complete love-making, the disturbance which is caused by the birth of the child is in no sense a danger to their happiness, but is its crown and completion.

A man once said to me – 'One can endure anything for the sake of a beloved wife.' But the *wife* is only utterly beloved when she and her married lover have not only entered paradise together, but when she fully realises, through insight gained by her own experiences, the true nature of that of which she is depriving her husband so long as her bodily condition makes sex-union with him impossible.

Much has been written, and may be found in the innumerable books on the sex-problems, as to whether a man and woman should or should not have relations while the wife is bearing an unborn child. In this matter experience is very various, so that it is difficult or impossible to give definite advice without knowing the full circumstances of each case.

When, however, we observe the admirable sanctity of the pregnant females of the woodland creatures, and when we consider the extraordinary ignorance and disregard of woman's needs which mark so many of our modern customs, we cannot but think that the safe side of this debatable question must be in the complete continence of the woman for at least six months before the birth of the child. I have heard from a number of women, however, that they desire union urgently at this time; and from others that the thought of it is incredible.

Tolstoy strongly condemned any sex contact while the wife was pregnant or nursing, and blames the husband who 'puts upon her the unbearable burden of being at one and the same time a mistress, an exhausted mother, and a sickly, irritable, hysterical individual. And the husband loves her as his mistress, ignores her as a mother, and hates her for the irritability and hysteria which he himself has produced and produces.' His view is taken by many of our noblest men.

While the wife feels that she cannot allow her husband to enter the portals of her body when it has become the sacred temple of a developing life, she should also consider the perpetual strain which nature imposes upon him; and the tender and loving wife will readily find some means of giving him that physical relief which his nature needs.

The exquisite, unselfish tenderness which is aroused in a man by the sense of mental and spiritual harmony with a wife who sympathises with, because she understands, his needs is one of the loveliest things in marriage. The wife who knows how to waken this tenderness in a man raises him out of the self-centred slough in which so many men wallow unhappily.

With an ardent man, wholly devoted to his wife and long deprived of her, the time will come when it will be sufficient for him to be near her and caress her for relief to take place without any physical connection.

After the birth of the first child the health of the mother and of the baby both demand that there should be no hurried beginning of a second. *At least* a year should pass before the second little life is allowed to begin its unfolding, so that *a minimum* of about two years should elapse before the second child is born.

The importance of this, both for the mother and for the child, is generally adequately recognised by medical specialists, and some distinguished gynaecologists advocate as much as three or five years between the births of successive children. While in the whole human relation there is no slavery or torture so horrible as coerced, unwilling motherhood, there is no joy and pride greater than that of a woman who is bearing the developing child of a man she adores. It is a serious reflection on our poisoned 'civilisation' that a pregnant woman should feel shame to appear in the streets. Never will the race reach true health till it is cured of its prurient sickness, and the prospective mother can carry her sacred burden as a priestess in a triumphal procession.

Of the innumerable problems which touch upon the qualities transmitted to the children by their parents, the study of which may be covered by the general term Eugenics, I shall here say nothing: nor shall I deal with the problems of birth and child-rearing. Many writers have considered these subjects, and my purpose in this book is to present aspects of sex-life which have been more or less neglected by others.

While throughout I have omitted the consideration of abnormalities, there is one condition which verges on the abnormal but yet touches the lives of some married people who are individually both normal and healthy, about which a few words need to be said.

It not infrequently happens that two healthy, loving people, for no apparent reason, seem unable to have a child.

The old-fashioned view was that the fault lay with the woman, and the reproach of being a barren woman is one which brought untold anguish to many hearts. It is now beginning to be recognised, however, that in a childless union the 'fault', if fault it be, is as often the man's as the woman's, particularly where the husband is a brain worker in a city.

Though it is natural that there should not be the same joy for the pair in a child which had not arisen from their own supreme fusion, nevertheless, the man who is generous and broadminded might find much joy in a child of his wife's were the obtaining of this child not coupled with the yielding of her body to the embrace of another man, which is so generally and so naturally repugnant to a husband. The future possibilities of science here come in. Much interesting research has already been done on the growth of the young of various creatures without the ordinary fertilisation of the mother egg-cell. Then there are the experiments by the famous Dr Hunter at the end of the eighteenth century, and more recent work. See, for instance, Heape, in the *Proceedings of the Royal Society*, 1897, and Marshall's text-book of *The Physiology of Reproduction*, 1910.

While in such an event as these discoveries adumbrate, the husband would have no bodily part in the heritage of the child, yet in the creation of its spirit he could play a profound part, the potentialities of which appear to be almost unrecognised by humanity.

The idea that the soul and character of the child can be in any degree influenced by the mental status of the mother during the months of its development as an embryo within her body, is apt to be greeted with pure scepticism – for it is difficult of proof, and repugnant to the male intellect, now accustomed to explain life in terms of chemistry.

Yet all the wisest mothers whom I know vary only in the degree of their belief in this power of the mother. All are agreed in believing that the spiritual and mental condition and environment of the mother does profoundly affect the character and the mental and spiritual powers of the child.

An interesting fact which strengthens the woman's point of view, is quoted (though not in this connection) by Marshall,* who says: 'It has been found that immunity from disease may be acquired by young animals being suckled by a female which had previously become immune, the antibody to the disease being absorbed in the ingested milk.' This particular fact is explainable in terms of chemistry; but it seems to me more than rash for anyone in these days of hormones from ductless glands, to deny the possibility of mental states in the mother generating 'chemical messengers', which may impress permanent characters in the physiological reactions of the developing child. Ellis says (Vol. 6, *Sex and Society*, 1913): 'The mother is the child's

* See p. 566 of the text-book on *The Physiology of Reproduction*, pp. xvii., 706, 1910.

supreme parent, and during the period from conception to birth the hygiene of the future man can only be affected by influences which work through her.'

And Alfred Russel Wallace, the great naturalist, thought the transmission of mental influence neither impossible nor even very improbable.* I am convinced that it takes place all the time, moulding and influencing the hereditary factors.

Hence I suggest that the husband who is deprived of normal fatherhood may yet make the child of his wife's body partly his own, if his thoughts are with her intensely, supportingly, and joyously throughout the whole time of the unborn baby's growth. If he reads to her, plays beautiful music or takes her to hear it, and gives her the very best of his thoughts and aspirations, mystical though the conclusion may seem, he does attain an actual measure of fatherhood.

The converse is even more difficult, where the wife is really barren and the husband capable of having children with another woman. Then the attainment of children by the man is impossible without the collaboration of another woman in a manner not outwardly recognised by our laws and customs. Even if this is done, it is clear that to introduce the child of another woman into the home is demanding a much greater self-abnegation from the wife than is demanded from the husband in the situation we have just considered.

Many people whose ideals are very noble are yet strangely incapable of adapting the material acts of life to the real fulfilment of their ideals. Thus there is a section of our community which insists that there should be no restriction whatever of the number of children born to married people. They think any birth control immoral. They take their stand upon the statement that we have no right to destroy potential life. But if they would

---

* See his letter to the scientific journal *Nature* in the year 1893, August 24, pp. 389 and 390.

study a little human or animal physiology they would find that not only every celibate, but also every married man incessantly and inevitably wastes myriads of germs (see page 76) which had the potentiality of fusion with an ovum, and consequently could have produced a child had opportunity been given them. For the supposed sake of one or two of these myriad sperms which must naturally and inevitably die, they encourage the production of babies in rapid succession which are weakened by their proximity while they might have been sturdy and healthy had they been conceived further apart from each other.

Such people, while awake to the claims of the unborn, nay, even of the unconceived, are blind to the claims of the one who should be dearest of all to the husband, and for whose health and happiness he is responsible. A man swayed by archaic dogma will allow, even coerce, his wife to bear and bring forth an infant annually. Save where the woman is exceptional, each child following so rapidly on its predecessor, saps and divides the vital strength which is available for the making of the offspring. This generally lowers the vitality of each succeeding child, and surely even if slowly, may murder the woman who bears them.

Of course, the effects of this strain upon the woman vary greatly according to her original health and vitality, the conditions of her surroundings and the intensity of the family's struggle for food. A half-starved mother trying to bring up children in the foul air of city slums, loses, as a rule, far more of her family than a comfortable and well-fed woman in the country. Nevertheless, conditions are not everything; under the best conditions, the chances of death of the later children of a large family, which comes rapidly, are far greater than for the earlier children.

Dr Ploetz found that while the death-rate of first-born infants is about 220 per thousand, the death-rate of the seventh-born is about 330, and of the twelfth-born is 597 per thousand. So that when 'Nature' has its way, and twelve children come to sap a woman's vitality, so little strength has she that nearly 60 per cent of these later ones die. What a waste of vitality! What a hideous orgy of agony for the mothers to produce in anguish death-doomed, suffering infants!

Forel (*The Sexual Question*, 1908) says: 'It seems almost incredible that in some countries medical men who are not ashamed to throw young men into the arms of prostitution, blush when mention is made of anti-conceptional methods. This false modesty, created by custom and prejudice, waxes indignant at innocent things while it encourages the greatest infamies.'

It is important to observe that Holland, the country which takes *most* care that children shall be well and voluntarily conceived, has increased its survival-rate, and has thereby, not diminished, but increased its population, and has the lowest infant mortality in Europe. While in America, where the outrageous 'Comstock Laws' confuse wise scientific prevention with illegal abortion and label them both as 'obscene', thus preventing people from obtaining decent hygienic knowledge, horrible and criminal abortion is more frequent than in any other country.

It should be realised that all the proper, medical methods of controlling pregnancy consist, not in destroying an already growing embryo, but in preventing the male sperm from reaching the unfertilised egg cell. This may be done either by shutting the sperms away from the opening of the womb, or by securing the death of *all* (instead of the natural death of all but *one*) of the two to six hundred million sperms which enter the woman. Even when a child is allowed to grow in its mother, all these hundreds of millions of sperms are inevitably and naturally destroyed every time the man has an emission, and to add one more to these millions sacrificed by Nature is surely no crime! To kill quickly the ejaculated sperms which would otherwise die and decompose naturally, is a simple matter. Their minute and uncovered bodies are plasmolised in weak acid, such as vinegar and water, or by a solution of quinine, or by many other substances.

To those who protest that we have no right to interfere with the course of Nature, one must point out that the whole of civilisation, everything which separates man from animals, is an interference with what such people commonly call 'Nature'.

Nothing in the cosmos can be against Nature, for it all forms part of the great processes of the universe.

Actions differ, however, in their relative positions in the scale of things. Only those actions are worthy which lead the race onwards to a higher and fuller completion and the perfecting of its powers, which steer the race into the main current of that stream of life and vitality which courses through us and impels us forward.

It is a sacred duty of all who dare to hand on the awe-inspiring gift of life, to hand it on in a vessel as fit and perfect as they can fashion, so that the body may be the strongest and most beautiful instrument possible in the service of the soul they summon to play its part in the mystery of material being.

CHAPTER X

Society

Love is fed not by what it takes, but by what it gives, and that
excellent dual love of man and wife must be fed also by the
love they give to others.

Edward Carpenter

Man, even the commonplace modern man, is romantic. He
craves consciously or unconsciously for the freedom, the beauty,
and the adventure which his forefathers found in their virgin
forests. This craving, transmuted, changed out of recognition by
civilised life and modern circumstances, is yet a factor not to be
ignored in the relationship of the sexes.

The 'bonds of matrimony', so often referred to with ribald
laughter, touch, and perhaps secretly gall, even the most romantic and devoted husband. If to the sincere and friendly question:
'What is most difficult in married life for the man?' one gets the
sincere and rueful answer – that answer may be summed up in
the words 'perpetual propinquity'.

Of this, the wife, particularly if she be really in love, is seldom
fully aware. If her husband is her true lover, his tenderness and
real devotion will give him the wit to conceal it. But though
by concealment he may preserve the unruffled surface of their
happiness, yet the longing to be roving is not completely extingu-
ished. In the true lover this unspoken, unconscious longing is
perhaps less a desire to set out upon a fresh journey than a
longing to experience again the exquisite joy of the return; to
re-live the magic charm of the approach to the spot in which

the loved one is living her life, into the sacred separateness of which the lover breaks, and, like the Prince by his kiss, to stir her to fresh activity.

As will be realised by those who have understood the preceding chapters, each coming together of man and wife, even if they have been mated for many years, should be a fresh adventure; each winning should necessitate a fresh wooing.

Yet what a man often finds so hard is to come to that wooing with full ardour and with that complete sense of romance which alone can render it utterly delightful, if the woman he is to woo has been in a too uninterrupted and prosaic relation with him in the meantime.

Most men, of course, have their businesses apart from their homes, but in the home lives of the great mass of middle-class people the Victorian tradition still too largely preponderates, and the mated pair bore or deaden each other during the daily routine.

To a very thoughtful couple whom I have known, so precious was the sense of romantic joy in one another that they endeavoured to perpetuate it by living in different houses.

Such a measure, however, is not likely to suit many people, particularly where there are children. Yet even without bodily separation (which must always entail expense) or any measure of freedom not at everyone's command, much can be done to retain that sense of spiritual freedom in which alone the full joy of loving union can be experienced.

But even intellectual and spiritual freedom is often rendered impossible in present-day marriage.

The beautiful desire for ideal unity which is so strong in most hearts is perhaps the original cause of one of the most deadening features in many marriages. In the endeavour to attain the ideal unity, one or other partner consciously or unconsciously imposes his or her will and opinions first upon the wife or husband, and then upon the children as they grow up.

The typical self-opinionated male which this course develops, while a subject for laughter in plays and novels, a laughter which hastens his extermination, is yet by no means extinct. In his less exaggerated form such a man may often be an idealist, but he is essentially an idealist of narrow vision. The peace, the unity, for which he craves is superficially attained; but it takes acuter eyes than his to see that it is attained not by harmonious intermingling, but by super-position and destruction.

I have known a romantic man of this type, apparently unaware that he was encroaching upon his wife's personality, who yet endeavoured not only to choose her books and her friends for her, but 'prohibited' her from buying the daily newspaper to which she had been accustomed for years before her marriage, saying that one newspaper was enough for them both, and blandly ignoring the fact that he took it with him out of the house before she had an opportunity of reading it. This man posed to himself more successfully than to others, not only as a romantic man, but as a model husband; and he reproached his wife for jeopardising their perfect unity whenever she accepted an invitation in which he was not included.

On the other hand, in homes where the avowed desire is for the modern freedom of intellectual life for both partners, there is very frequently a bickering, a sense of disharmony and unrest that dispels the peace and the air of restful security which is an essential feature of a true home.

It is one of the most difficult things in the world for two people of different opinions to retain their own opinions without each endeavouring to convert or coerce the other, and at the same time to feel the same tender trust in the judgment of the other that each would have felt had they agreed.

It takes a generous and beautiful heart to see beauty and dignity in the attitude of a mate who is looking at the other side of a vital question.

But the very fact that it *does* take a beautiful and generous heart to do this thing proves it well worth the doing.

If the easier way is chosen and the two mutually conceal their views when they differ, or the stronger partner coerces the weaker into hiding those traits which give personality to an individual, the result is an impoverishing of both, and through that very fact, an impoverishment, a lowering of the love which both sought to serve.

In marriage each one dreams that he will find the Understander – the one from whom he may set out into the world in search of treasures of knowledge and experience, and before whom the spoils may be exhibited without thought of rivalry, and with the certainty of glad apprisal. Treasures, dear to our own hearts but of no value to others, should here find appreciation, and here the tender super-sensitive germ of an idea may be watered and tended till its ripe beauty is ready to burst upon the world.

As marriage is at present such tenderness and such stimulating appreciation is much more likely to come from the woman to the man and his work than from the man to the woman. For too long have men been accustomed to look upon woman's views, and in particular on her intellectual opinions, as being something demanding at the most a bland humouring beneath the kindest smiles.

Even from the noblest man, the woman of sensitive personality today feels an undercurrent as of surprised congratulation when she has anything to say worth his *serious* attention outside that department of life supposed to belong to her 'sphere'. Thus man robs his wedded self of a greatness which the dual unity might reach.

But in marriage the mutual freedom and respect for opinion, vitally important though it be, is not sufficient for the full development of character. Life demands ever-widening interests. Owing partly to the differentiation of many types of individuals due to the specialisation of civilisation, which interests thoughtful individuals, and partly to the transmutation of his old vagrant instinct, man increasingly desires to touch and to realise the lives of his fellows. In the lives of others our hearts and understandings may find perpetual adventures into the new and strange.

Individual human beings, even the noblest and most complex yet evolved, have but a share of the innumerable faculties of the race. Hence even in a supremely happy marriage, which touches, as does the mystic in his raptures, a realisation of the whole universe, there cannot lie the *whole* of life's experience. Outside the actual lives of the pair there must always be many types of thought and many potentialities which can only be realised in the lives of other people.

In the complete human relation friends of all grades are needed, as well as a mate. Marriage, however, in its present form is too often made to curtail the enjoyment of intimate friendships. The reason for this is partly the social etiquette, which, though discarded in the highest levels of society, still lingers in many circles, of inviting the husband and the wife together upon all social occasions. It is true that they are separated at the dinner table, but they are always within the possibility of earshot of each other, which very often deadens their potentialities for being entertaining. The mere fact of being overheard repeating something one may have already said elsewhere is sufficient to prevent some people from telling their best stories, or from expressing their real views upon important matters.

And, still more serious barrier to joy, so primitive, so little evolved are we even yet, there is in most human beings a strong streak of sex-jealousy. For either mate to be allowed to go out uncriticised into the world, is to demand, if not more than the other is willing to give, at least a measure of trust which by its rarity appears nowadays as something conspicuously fine.

Jealousy, which is one of the most frequent shadows cast by the blight of love, is very apt to sow a distrust in one which makes a normal life for the other partner impossible.

It is hard to say in which sex the feeling is more strongly developed. It takes special forms under different circumstances, and if a nature is predisposed towards it, it is one of the most difficult characteristics to eradicate.

Custom, and generations of traditions, seem to have imprinted on our race the false idea that marital fidelity is to be strengthened by coercive bonds. We are slowly growing out of this, and nowadays in most books giving advice to young wives there is a section telling them that a man should be allowed his men friends after marriage.

But this is not enough. There should be complete and unquestioning trust on both sides. The man and the woman should each be free to go unchallenged by a thought on solitary excursions, or on visits, weekends or walking tours, without the possibility of a breath of jealousy or suspicion springing up in the heart of one or the other.

It is true that many natures are not yet ready for such trust, and might abuse such freedom. But the baser natures will always find a method of gratifying their desires, and are not likely to err more in trusted freedom than they would inevitably have done through secret intrigues if held in jealous bondage.

While, on the other hand, it is only in the fresh unsullied air of such freedom that the fullest and most perfect love can develop. In the marriage relation it is supremely true that only by loosening the bonds can one bind two hearts indissolubly together.

When they are sometimes physically apart married lovers attain the closest spiritual union. For with sensitive spirits — and they are the only ones who know the highest pinnacles of love — periods of separation and solitude can be revivifying and recreative.

So great is the human soul that some of its beauty is hidden by nearness: it needs distance between it and the beholder to be perceived in its true perspective.

To the realisation of the beauty and the enjoyment of solitude, woman in general tends to be less awake than man. This, perhaps, is due to the innumerable generations during which the claims of her children and of domestic life have robbed her of Nature's healing gift.

Although it is merely incidental to the drama, yet to me the most poignant thing in Synge's beautiful play *Deirdré* is that she could feel inevitable tragedy when the first thought of something apart from herself crosses her lover's mind. Deirdré and her lover had been together for seven years in an unbroken and idyllic intimacy, and she feels that all is finished, and that her doom, the knell of their joy, had struck, when for the first time she perceived in him a half-formed thought of an occupation apart from her.

This ancient weakness of her sex must be conquered, and is being conquered by the modern woman.

While modern marriage is tending to give ever more and more freedom to each of the partners, there is at the same time a unity of work and interest growing up which brings them together on a higher plane than the purely domestic one which was so confining to the women and so dull to the men. Every year one sees a widening of the independence and the range of the pursuits of women: but still, far too often, marriage puts an end to woman's intellectual life. Marriage can never reach its full stature until women possess as much intellectual freedom and freedom of opportunity within it as do their partners.

That at present the majority of women neither desire freedom for creative work, nor would know how to use it, is only a sign that we are still living in the shadow of the coercive and dwarfing influences of the past.

In an interesting article on woman's intellectual work, W. Thomas (*Sex and Society*, 1907) says:

The American woman, with the enjoyment of greater lib-
erty, has made an approach toward the standards of professional scholarship, and some individuals stand at the very
top in their university studies and examinations. The trouble
with these cases is that they are either swept away and
engulfed by the modern system of marriage, or find themselves excluded in some intangible way from association
with men in the fullest sense, and no career open to their
talents.

He sees clearly that this is but a passing phase in the development of our society, and he advocates a wider scope for the play
of married women's powers.

The practice of an occupational activity of her own choos-
ing, and a generous attitude towards this on the part of
the man, would contribute to relieve the strain and make
marriage more frequently successful.

When woman naturally develops the powers latent within her,
man will find at his side not only a mate, free and strong, but a
desirable friend and an intellectual comrade.
The desire for freedom, both for physical and mental exploration and for experiences outside the sacred enclosure of the
home, may at first sight appear to be conflicting and entirely
incompatible with the ideal of closer and more perfect unity
between the married pair. But this conflict is only apparent,
though it is true that most writers have failed to realise this.
Consequently in some sections of the writing and teaching of the
'advanced' schools there are claims only for increased freedom –
a freedom to wander at will – a freedom in which the wanderer
does not return to his fixed centre.
On the other hand there are those who realise principally the
beauty of married unity, and, concentrating on the demand for
the unity and extremest stability on the part of the married
pair, are very apt to ignore the enriching flow of a wide life's

experiences. They try to dam up the fertilising tide of life, and thus, though they are unconscious of what they are doing, they tend to reduce the richness and beauty of marriage.

It is for the young people of the new generation to realise that the two currents of longing which spring up within them – the longing for a full life-experience and the longing for a close union with a lifelong mate – are not incompatible, but are actually both essential parts of the more perfect and fuller beauty of the future that already seeks to find its expression in their lives.

Ellen Key (*Love and Marriage*) seems to fear the widening of the married woman's life, and she writes as though the aspiration to do professional and intellectual work of a high order must dwarf and sterilise the mother in the married woman.

She writes of a more northerly people, the Scandinavians, and it may be true of her countrywomen, I do not know. But it is *not* essentially and universally true. I am writing of the English, the English of today, and though we also have among us that dwarfed and sterilised type of woman, she forms in our community a dwindling minority. The majority of our best women enter marriage and motherhood, or else long for a marriage more beautiful than the warped mockery of it that is offered them.

As Mrs Stetson says (*Women and Economics*):

In the primal physical functions of maternity the human female cannot show that her supposed specialisation to these uses has improved her fulfilment of them, rather the opposite. The more freely the human mother mingles in the natural industries of a human creature, as in the case of the savage woman, the peasant woman, the working woman everywhere who is not overworked, the more rightly she fulfils these functions.

The more absolutely the woman is segregated to sex-functions only, cut off from all economic use and made wholly dependent on the sex-relation as means of a livelihood, the more pathological does her motherhood become. The over-development of sex caused by her economic dependence on the male reacts unfavourably on her essential duties. She is too female for the perfect motherhood!

The majority of our young women, I am convinced, have in them the potentiality of a full and perfected love. So, too, have the majority of our young men. For the best type of young man today is tired of polygamy; he has seen enough in his father's and friends' lives of the weariness of the sinister, secret polygamy, that hides itself and rots the race under the protecting cloak of the supposed monogamy of our social system.

But as things are at present in England, the young man who marries, however much he may be in love, is generally too ignorant (as has been indicated in the preceding chapters) to give his wife all her nature requires. Then, sooner or later, comes the sequence of disappointments which culminate in the longing for a fresh adventure.

As one young husband said to me, 'A decent man can't go on having unions with his wife when she obviously does not enjoy them,' and so he is forced to 'go elsewhere'. 'And they call us polygamists! We are not polygamists any longer. But marriage is a rotten failure,' was his verdict.

No. They are not polygamists, the finest young men of the present and of the future. Most men today are not in their heart of hearts polygamists, in spite of all the outward signs to the contrary; in spite of the fact that so few of them have remained faithful to one woman. But they are ignorant of the sex-laws and traditions, that sex-knowledge which was the heritage of much less civilised tribes, and so they have trampled and crushed out the very thing for the growth of which their hearts are aching.

Hence secretly (for in a marriage that is at least superficially happy the man seldom does this openly) the man begins to crave for another type of society and he 'goes elsewhere'. Not, it is true, to find, or even in the hope of finding, what he would get from a perfect marriage; but often to satisfy in some measure that yearning for fresh experience, for romance, and for that sense of fusion with another in the romantic experience which, even if it is only a delusion of the senses, is yet one of the most precious things life has to offer.

It is hard, indeed in many cases it seems impossible, for a good woman to understand what it is that draws her husband from her. Restricted by habit and convention in the exercise of her faculties, she is unaware of the ever-narrowing range of her interest and her powers of conversation. The home life tends to become that of a fenced pond, instead of a great ocean with innumerable currents. From the restricted and fenced, man's instinct is ever to escape. Man's opportunities for exploration in the cities are few, and the prostitute is one of the most obvious doors of escape into new experiences.

Women feel a so righteous and instinctive horror of prostitution, and regarding it they experience an indignation so intense, that they do not seek to understand the man's attitude.

The prostitute, however, sometimes supplies an element which is not purely physical, and which is often lacking in the wife's relation with her husband, an element of charm and mutual gaiety in pleasure.

If good women realised this, while they would judge and endeavour to eliminate prostitution no less strenuously, they might be in a better position to begin their efforts to free men from the hold that social disease has upon them.

It is perhaps impossible to find the beginning of a vicious circle, but the first step out of it must be the realisation that one is within it, and the realisation of some, at any rate, of its component parts.

Man, through prudery, through the custom of ignoring the woman's side of marriage and considering his own whim as marriage law, has largely lost the art of stirring a chaste partner to physical love. He therefore deprives her of a glamour, the loss of which he deplores, for he feels a lack not only of romance and beauty, but of something higher which is mystically given as the result of the complete union. He blames his wife's 'coldness' instead of his own want of art. Then he seeks elsewhere for the things she could have given him had he known how to win them. And she, knowing that the shrine has been desecrated, is filled with righteous indignation, though generally as blind as he is to the true cause of what has occurred.

Manifold and far-reaching, influencing the whole structure of society not only in this country, but in every country and at every time, have been the influences which have grown up from the root-fallacy in the marriage relation.

Then there is another cause for the dulling of a wife's bright charm – her inferior position in the eyes of the law. It is indeed a serious matter, as Jean Finot says, 'that, under present conditions, the mistress keeps certain liberties which are denied to married women.'

The past and its history have been studied by many, and we may leave it. What concerns the present generation of young married people is today and the future. The future is full of hope. Already one sees beginning to grow up a new relationship between the units composing society.

In the noblest society love will hold sway. The love of mates will always be the supremest life experience, but it will no longer be an experience exclusive and warped.

The love of friends and children, of comrades and fellow-workers, will but serve to develop every power of the two who are mates. By mingling the greatness of their individual stature they can achieve together something that, had both or either been dwarfed and puny individuals, would have remained for ever unattainable.

The whole trend of the evolution of human society has been toward an increased coherence of all its parts, until at the present time it is already almost possible to say that the community has an actual life on a plane above that of all the individuals composing it: that the community, in fact, is a super-entity. It is through the community of human beings, and not in our individual lives, that we reach an ultimate permanence upon this globe.

When our relation to the community is fully realised, it will be seen that the health, the happiness, and the consequent powers of every individual, concern not only his own life, but also affect the whole community of which he is a member.

The happiness of a perfect marriage, which enhances the vitality of the private life, renders one not only capable of adding to the stream of the life-blood of the community in children, but by marriage one is also rendered a fitter and more perfect instrument for one's own particular work, the results of which should be shared by society as a whole, and in the tempering and finishing of which society plays a part.

Thus it is the concern of the whole community that marriage should be as perfect, and hence as joyous, as possible; so that the powers which should be set free and created for the purpose of the whole community should not be frittered away in the useless longing and disappointment engendered by ignorance, narrow restrictions, and low ideals.

In the world the happily mated pair should be like a great and beautiful light; a light not hid under a bushel, but one whose beams shine through the lives of all around them.

CHAPTER XI

The Glorious Unfolding

Let knowledge grow from more to more, but more of reverence
in us dwell.
Tennyson

We are surrounded in this world by processes and transmutations so amazing that were they not taking place around us
hourly they would be scouted as impossible imaginings.

A mind must be dull and essentially lacking in wonderment
which, without amazement, can learn for the first time that the
air we breathe, apparently so uniform in its invisible unity, is in
reality composed of two principal, and several other, gases. The
two gases, however, are but mixed as wine may be with water,
and each gas by itself is a colourless air, visually like that mixture
of the two which we call the atmosphere.

Much greater is the miracle of the composition of water. It is
made of only two gases, one of them a component of the air we
breathe, and the other similarly invisible and odourless, but far
lighter. These two invisible gases, when linked in a proportion
proper to their natures, fuse and are no longer ethereal and
invisible, but precipitate in a new substance – water.

The waves of the sea with their thundering power, the spark-
ling tides of the river buoying the ships, are but the transmuted
resultants of the union of two invisible gases. And this, in its
simplest terms, is a parable of the infinitely complex and amazing
transmutations of married love.

Ellis expresses the strange mystery of one of the physical sides of love when he says:

> What has always baffled men in the contemplation of sexual love is the seeming inadequacy of its cause, the immense discrepancy between the necessarily circumscribed regions of mucous membrane which is the final goal of such love and the sea of world-embracing emotions to which it seems the door, so that, as Remy de Gourmont has said, 'the mucous membranes, by an ineffable mystery, enclose in their obscure folds all the riches of the infinite.' It is a mystery before which the thinker and the artist are alike overcome.

To me, however, the recent discoveries of physiology seem to afford a key which may unlock a chamber of the mystery and admit us to one of the halls of the palace of truth. The hormones (see page 92) in each individual body pour from one organ and affect another, and thus influence the whole character of the individual's life processes. The visible secretions and the most subtle essences which pass during union between man and woman, affect the lives of each and are essentially vital to each other. As I see them, the man and the woman are each organs, parts, of the other. And in the strictest scientific, as well as in a mystical, sense they *together* are a single unit, an individual entity. There is a *physiological* as well as a spiritual truth in the words 'they twain shall be one flesh.'

In love it is not only that the yearning of the bonds of affinity to be satisfied is met by the linking with another, but that out of this union there grows a new and unprecedented creation.

In this I am not speaking of the bodily child which springs from the love of its parents, but of the super-physical entity created by the perfect union in love of man and woman. Together, united by the love bonds which hold them, they are a new and wondrous thing surpassing, and different from, the arithmetical sum of them both when separate.

So seldom has the perfection of this new creation been experienced, that we are still far short even of imagining its full potentialities, but that it must have mighty powers we dimly realise.

Youths and maidens stirred by the attraction of love, feel hauntingly and inarticulately that there is before them an immense and beautiful experience: feel as though in union with the beloved there will be added powers of every sort which have no measure in terms of the ordinary unmated life.

These prophetic dreams, if they are not true of each individual life, are yet true of the race as a whole. For in the dreams of youth today is a foreshadowing of the reality of the future.

So accustomed have we recently become to accept one aspect of organic evolution, that we tend to see in youth only a recapitulation of our race's history. The well-worn phrase 'Ontogeny repeats Phylogeny' has helped to concentrate our attention on the fact that the young in their development, in ourselves as in the animals, go through many phases which resemble the stages through which the whole race must have passed in the course of its evolution.

While this is true, there is another characteristic of youth: It is prophetic!

The dreams of youth, which each young heart expects to see fulfilled in its own life, seem so often to fade unfulfilled. But that is because the wonderful powers of youth are not supplied with the necessary tool – knowledge. And so potentialities, which could have worked miracles, are allowed to atrophy and die.

But as humanity orients itself more truly, more and more will the knowledge and experience of the whole race be placed at the disposal of all youth on its entry into life.

Then that glorious upspringing of the racial ideal, which finds its expression in each unspoiled generation of youth, will at last meet with a store of knowledge sufficient for its needs, and will find ready as a tool to its hand the accumulated and sifted wisdom of the race.

Then youth will be spared the blunders and the pain and the unconscious self-destruction that today leaves scarcely anyone untouched.

In my own life, comparatively short and therefore lacking in experience though it be, I have known both personally and vicariously so much anguish that might have been prevented by knowledge. This impels me not to wait till my experience and researches are complete, and my life and vital interest are fading, but to hand on at once those gleanings of wisdom I have already accumulated which may help the race to understand itself. Hence I conclude this little book, for, though incomplete, it contains some of the vital things youth should be told.

In all life activities, house-building, hunting or any other, where intellectual and oral tradition comes in, as it does with the human race, 'instinct' tends to die out. Thus the human mother is far less able to manage her baby without instruction than is a cat her kittens; although the human mother at her best has, in comparison with the cat, an infinitude of duties toward, and influences over, her child.

A similar truth holds in relation to marriage. The century-long following of various 'civilised' customs has not only deprived our young people of most of the instinctive knowledge they might have possessed, but has given rise to innumerable false and polluting customs.

Though many write on the art of managing children, few have anything to say about the art of marriage, save those who have some dogma, often theological or subversive of natural law, to proclaim.

Any fundamental truth regarding marriage is rendered immeasurably difficult to ascertain because of the immense ranges of variety in human beings, even of the same race, many of which result from the artificial conditions and the unnatural stimuli so prevalent in what we call civilisation. To attempt anything like a serious study of marriage in all its varieties would be a monumental work. Those who have even partially undertaken it have tended to become entangled in a maze of abnormalities, so that the needs of the normal, healthy, romantic person have been overlooked.

Each pair, therefore, has tended to repeat the blunders from which it might have been saved, and to stumble blindly in a maze of difficulties which are not the essential heritage of humanity, but are due to the unreasoning folly of our present customs.

I have written this book for those who enter marriage normally and healthily, and with optimism and hope.

If they learn its lessons they may be saved from some of the pitfalls in which thousands have wrecked their happiness, but they must not think that they will thereby easily attain the perfection of marriage. There are myriad subtleties in the adjustment of any two individuals.

Each pair must, using the tenderest and most delicate touches, sound and test each other, learning their way about the intricacies of each other's hearts.

Sometimes, with all the knowledge and the best will in the world, two who have married find that they cannot fuse their lives; of this tragedy I have not here anything to say; but ordinary unhappiness would be less frequent than it is were the tenderness of *knowledge* applied to the problem of mutual adjustment from the first day of marriage.

All the deepest and highest forces within us impel us to evolve an ever nobler and tenderer form of life-long monogamy as our social ideal. While the thoughtful and tenderhearted must seek, with ever greater understanding, to ease and comfort those who miss this joyful natural development, reformers in their zeal for side-issues must not forget the main growth of the stock. The beautiful sense for love in the hearts of the young should be encouraged, and they should have access to the knowledge of how to cultivate it, instead of being diverted by the clamour for 'freedom' to destroy it.

Disillusioned middle age is apt to look upon the material side of the marriage relation, to see its solid surface in the cold, dull light of everyday experience; while youth, irradiated by the glow of its dreams, is unaware how its aerial and celestial phantasies are broken and shattered when unsuspectingly brought up against the hard facts of physical reality.

The transmutation of material facts by celestial phantasies is to some extent within the power of humanity, even the imperfect humanity of today.

When knowledge and love together go to the making of each marriage, the joy of *that new unit, the pair* will reach from the physical foundations of its bodies to the heavens where its head is crowned with stars.

NOTE

While I believe that the charts I give of the Law of Periodicity of recurrence of desire truly represent the fundamental rhythm of average healthy women, it must be remembered that my theory is new, and every well-authenticated case for or against it will be valuable. I invite letters from those who can confirm, qualify, or correct my views from their own experience. To obtain scientific knowledge the largest possible number of individual cases must be studied. All communications will be treated with the strictest confidence.

Dr M. C. STOPES
c/o Mr A. C. Fifield
13, Clifford's Inn, London EC4

Appendix

NOTE 1. (See page 59.)

For suffering and even death of unmated females, see e.g. Marshall, in *Quarterly Journal Microscopical Society*, Vol. 48, 1904, p. 323; Parsons, in *British Medical Journal*, October, 1904.

NOTE 2. (See page 65.)

A frequent mistake (made even by gynaecologists) is to confuse menstruation with the 'period of desire' which is generally called 'heat' in animals. Even in the most authoritative recent text books, such phrases as 'heat and menstruation' are very common, thus coupling heat and menstruation as though they were equivalents, while the older books quite explicitly look on the menstrual period in women as corresponding to desire or 'heat' in animals. This error has even been repeated very recently in the *Proceedings* of the Royal Society of Medicine.*

Some physiologists have studied this subject in several of the higher animals, and now realise that the time of desire is physiologically distinct from the phase which is represented by menstruation in women. It seems to be fairly well established that in women menstruation is caused by an internal secretion of the

* See Dr Raymond Crawfurd's mistaken statement that 'the identity of œstrus, or "heat" in the lower animals and of menstruation in the human female, admits of no doubt.' *Proc.* Roy. Soc. Medicine, vol. 9, 1916, p. 62.

ovaries (c.f. pages 92–3), and is not directly due to ovulation, though it must have some connection with it.*

The most that modern science appears to have attained is briefly summarised in the following quotation from Marshall (*The Physiology of Reproduction*, p. 69):

According to Martin and certain other writers, the human female often experiences a distinct post-menstrual œstrus [Modern research has recognised a period when the female animal is ready for impregnation, which is called the œstrus, and a preparatory series of physiological changes called the pro-estrous phase. – M.C.S.], at which sexual desire is greater than at other times; so that, although conception can occur throughout the intermenstrual period, it would seem probable that originally coition was restricted to definite periods of œstrus following menstrual or pro-estrous periods in women, as in females of other mammalia. On this point Heape writes as follows: 'This special time for œstrus in the human female has very frequently been denied, and, no doubt, modern civilisation and modern social life do much to check the natural sexual instinct where there is undue strain on the constitution, or to stimulate it at other times where extreme vigour is the result. For these reasons a definite period of œstrus may readily be interfered with, but the instinct is, I am convinced, still marked.'

In nearly all wild animals there is a definite period for sexual excitement, very commonly just at that time of the year which fits into the span of gestation, so that the young are born at the season which gives them the best chance to grow up. In animals

* The best modern account of these complex subjects will be found in the advanced text-book *The Physiology of Reproduction*, pp. xvii., 706, by F. H. A. Marshall. Reference may be made to original papers by J. Beard in the *Anat. Anzeiger.* for 1897; and by Heape in the *Philosophical Trans. Royal Society*, 1894, 97.

he period of desire, the ovulation (or setting free of the female germ or unfertilised egg-cell) and the time of the birth of the young, are all co-related harmoniously. The male animal is only allowed to approach the female when the natural longing for union is upon her. Among human beings, the only race which seems to have long periods of sexual quiescence at all comparable with those natural to the animals are the Esquimaux, who appear to pass many months without any unions of the men and women.